# Magnesium
## and
## Its  Alloys

New York
London

# Magnesium

# and

# Its Alloys

by

## C. Sheldon Roberts

FAIRCHILD SEMICONDUCTOR CORPORATION
PALO ALTO, CALIFORNIA

**John Wiley & Sons, Inc.**

# Preface

The commercial status of magnesium both as a structural metal and as a versatile chemical has been established. Publications of original scientific and engineering studies of magnesium and its alloys are now appearing at a rate of more than one hundred per year in the technical literature of the world. Many books have been written about magnesium. Most of them are listed in the bibliography. Each author has approached the subject in a different way—some specialized, some popularized, some oriented to design or shop practices. I have tried to make this a reference book of broad scope and concise presentation. It should be of use to the modern metallurgist, physicist, chemist, or engineer needing either isolated facts or a general picture of the science and technology of this fascinating metal. It is not intended as a shop manual or as a handbook for the structural designer. Design, fabrication, and finishing of magnesium alloy structures have been explained authoritatively in frequently revised commercial literature. However, the time appears ripe for the publication of an up-to-date and comprehensive magnesium reference book. Research since the publication of Adolf Beck's classic volume in 1939 has clarified greatly our understanding of magnesium and has augmented process and alloy development.

In the attempt to satisfy an apparent need, I have tried primarily to present clearly the knowledge of scientific properties and technology, to emphasize uncertainties which need to be resolved, and to link the two areas in more than a casual manner. I have tried to minimize the inclusion of highly controversial material and to qualify it properly when it is presented. Unfortunately, the reader may find favorite or interesting subjects missing for this reason. I have not included in Chapter 1 property values which are doubtful, values from material of low or unknown purity when purity is important, or surface properties which have not been measured on closely defined surfaces. Much remains yet to be measured with precision. The relative scantiness of Chapter 5 emphasizes the need for more research in the area of solid-state diffusion and diffusion-controlled processes. I have tried to clarify the interesting complexity of the deformation of magnesium in Chapter 4. This is another area where more changes are rather certain to appear in the future. I have avoided the tabulation of all but the most important properties of commercial alloys. More complete alloy property data are available in the commercial literature. New alloys will be developed continually and old ones will drop into obsolescence.

The technological details in the last four chapters admittedly are strongly associated with United States practice, in particular that of The Dow Chemical Company. However, I have attempted to give this book some international flavor by referring to the intensive early development of magnesium science in Germany, the important contributions of the British in modern casting alloy development, the outstanding stimulus to advanced metal purification supplied by the Canadian industry, as well as the daring and the successful move in the United States to bring magnesium products to high-volume production.

I have avoided a heavy historical emphasis mainly because of a desire to stress the importance of the present position and what it means for the future. The history of magnesium technology will continue to be described more adequately by those who have had the honor of participating in its development for many years. The articles by C. J. P. Ball, W. H. Dow, and J. D. Hanawalt listed in the bibliography are of special interest from the historical standpoint.

The intriguing metallography of magnesium is described splendidly in a book by Bulian and Fahrenhorst, also listed in the bibliography. For this reason I have not dealt with it here.

C. Sheldon Roberts

*Los Altos, California,*
*1958*

# Acknowledgment

Many former colleagues in The Dow Chemical Company have helped me even more than I had expected. I thank them for generous and constructive criticisms, original material, and moral support. I could not have written a volume of this completeness without their help. Contribution of original source material is credited in the text. In particular, I am grateful to R. S. Busk for his untiring and valuable criticism of the entire manuscript, to M. R. Bothwell for criticism and contributions to Chapter 8, to J. B. Clark for criticism and material for Chapters 3 and 5, to S. L. Couling for contributions and criticism of Chapters 4 and 7, to J. W. Fredrickson for criticism of Chapter 1, to F. J. Krenzke for suggestions concerning Chapter 9, to D. L. Leman and T. E. Leontis for criticism of Chapters 6 and 7, to K. E. Nelson for criticism of Chapter 6, to J. L. Nichols for references and criticism, to L. Sturkey for patient criticism of many chapters, and to L. Whitby for suggestions concerning Chapter 8.

In addition, thanks are due for illustrative material to Commander R. E. Reed-Hill, American Institute of Mining and Metallurgical Engineers, American Society for Metals, *Acta Metallurgica, Czechoslovak Journal of Physics, Journal of the Institute of Metals,* McGraw-Hill Book Company, *Modern Metals, Physical Review,* Publishing House of the USSR Academy of Science, The Royal Society, Wright Air Development Center, and *Zeitschrift fur anorganischen Chemie.*

Finally, it is a pleasure to thank Patricia W. Roberts for many hours of active support with the typewriter as well as for much of the moral support that every author needs.

C. S. R.

# Contents

**1  Physical Properties of Magnesium**                1

1.1  Atomic Properties     1
1.2  Structural Properties     4
1.3  Thermal, Electrical, and Magnetic Properties     9


**2  Alloy Theory and Properties**                17

2.1  The Empirical Theory of Magnesium Alloys     17
2.2  Electron Theories of Magnesium     21
2.3  Binary Solid Solubility and Lattice Parameters     26
2.4  Intermetallic Compound Characteristics     34
2.5  Ordering in Solid Solutions     37


**3  Magnesium Alloy Systems**                42

3.1  Mg-Ag     43        3.9   Mg-Cu    51
3.2  Mg-Al     44        3.10  Mg-Fe    52
3.3  Mg-Au     45        3.11  Mg-Ga    52
3.4  Mg-Ba     46        3.12  Mg-Ge    53
3.5  Mg-Bi     47        3.13  Mg-Hg    54
3.6  Mg-Ca     48        3.14  Mg-K     55
3.7  Mg-Cd     49        3.15  Mg-La    55
3.8  Mg-Ce     50        3.16  Mg-Li    56

3.17 Mg-Mn     57                  3.26 Mg-Zn     66
3.18 Mg-Na     58                  3.27 Mg-Zr     67
3.19 Mg-Ni     59                  3.28 Mg-Al-Ca     68
3.20 Mg-Pb     60                  3.29 Mg-Al-Zn     71
3.21 Mg-Sb     61                  3.30 Mg-Li-Al     74
3.22 Mg-Si     62                  3.31 Mg-Li-Zn     77
3.23 Mg-Sn     63                  3.32 Mg-Th-Zn     79
3.24 Mg-Th     64                  3.33 Mg-Th-Zr     80
3.25 Mg-Tl     65

## 4   The Deformation of Magnesium                                  81

4.1   Elastic and Anelastic Deformation     81
4.2   Plastic Deformation by Slip     84
4.3   Plastic Deformation by Twinning     88
4.4   Compression Banding     94
4.5   Grain Boundary Deformation     95
4.6   The Phenomenology of Plastic Deformation     95
4.7   Ductility and Fracture     107

## 5   Time-Temperature-Dependent Alloy Phenomena          108

5.1   Diffusion     108
5.2   Recrystallization and Grain Growth     110
5.3   Precipitation     117

## 6   Casting Alloys and Technology                              126

6.1   Introduction     126
6.2   Magnesium-Aluminum-Based Casting Alloys     133
6.3   The Addition of Zirconium to Magnesium Alloys     135
6.4   Magnesium-Zinc-Based Casting Alloys     136
6.5   Magnesium–Rare-Earth-Metal–Based Casting Alloys     137
6.6   Magnesium-Thorium-Based Casting Alloys     139
6.7   The Melting of Magnesium Alloys     141
6.8   Grain Refinement     144
6.9   The Sand Casting of Magnesium Alloys     144
6.10  The Permanent Mold and Pressure Die Casting of
         Magnesium Alloys     149

## 7  Wrought Alloys and Technology                              154

7.1  Introduction     154
7.2  Magnesium-Manganese- and Magnesium-Aluminum-Based
       Wrought Alloys     159
7.3  Magnesium-Zinc-Based Wrought Alloys   161
7.4  Magnesium-Thorium-Based Wrought Alloys     163
7.5  Production of Ingot     168
7.6  The Rolling of Magnesium Alloy     171
7.7  The Extrusion of Magnesium     177
7.8  The Forging of Magnesium Alloys     181
7.9  Preferred Orientation     182

## 8  Chemical Properties and Applications                       194

8.1  Anodic Behavior of Magnesium     194
8.2  Corrosion of Magnesium Alloys     195
8.3  Protective Anodes     199
8.4  The Magnesium Dry Cell     202
8.5  Important Chemical Applications     204

## 9  The Extraction and Refining of Magnesium                   208

9.1  Raw Material Sources     208
9.2  The Electrolytic Reduction Processes     209
9.3  The Direct Reduction Processes     213
9.4  Production     215
9.5  Purity and Refining of Magnesium     219

## Bibliography                                                  223

## Index                                                        225

# 1

# Physical Properties of Magnesium

## 1.1  Atomic Properties

Magnesium, the second lightest divalent alkaline earth metal, is number 12 in the periodic table of the elements. The isotopes 24, 25, and 26 occur naturally in the proportions of about 7:1:1, giving an atomic weight of 24.32(2). The radioactive isotopes 23 and 27 have been found to have half-lives of 12.3 seconds and 9.58 minutes respec-

**Table 1.1.   Atomic Structure Factor, $f$, for Magnesium** [3]

| $(\sin \theta)/\lambda$ $(\lambda, A)$ | $f$ |
|:---:|:---:|
| 0 | 12 |
| 0.1 | 10.5 |
| 0.2 | 8.6 |
| 0.3 | 7.25 |
| 0.4 | 5.95 |
| 0.5 | 4.8 |
| 0.6 | 3.85 |
| 0.7 | 3.15 |
| 0.8 | 2.55 |
| 0.9 | 2.2 |
| 1.0 | 2.0 |
| 1.1 | 1.8 |

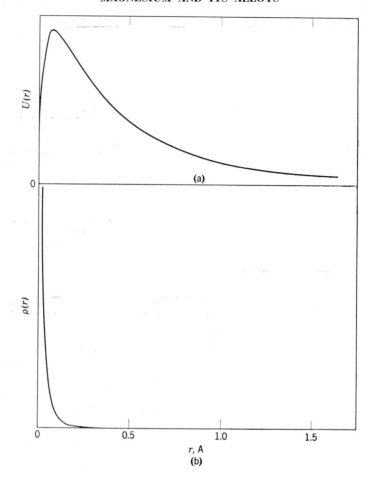

Fig. 1.1. (*a*) Radial electron distribution function $U(r)$ and (*b*) electron density $\rho(r)$ for free magnesium atom according to Thomas-Fermi theory.

tively. Sheline and Johnson [1] as well as Jones and Kohman [2] have reported the artificial production of useful quantities of the radioactive isotope 28 (half-life = 21.3 hours). This isotope has allowed the measurement of the self-diffusivity of magnesium, as is discussed in Section 5.1.

The twelve orbital electrons in the free atom occupy the states $1s^2 2s^2 2p^6 3s^2$. The optical spectra are well known and too complex to be described usefully here. The x-ray emission lines $K\alpha$ and $K\beta$ are at 9.889 and 9.558 A respectively. The $K$-absorption edge for x-rays is 9.512 A.   The atomic structure factor for x-ray scattering is useful in problems of crystal structure analysis.   The quantum mechanically calculated values of this factor at different values of $(\sin\theta)/\lambda$ according to James and Brindley [3] are given in Table 1.1 where $\theta$ is the angle of scattering and $\lambda$ is the x-ray wavelength.

The atomic structure factors were obtained by an interpolation method from specific calculations for neighboring atoms in the periodic table.   Apparently a calculation of the wave functions for the magnesium atom by the Hartree self-consistent field method [4] has never been published.   The radial electron distribution and the corresponding electron density as derived from the Thomas-Fermi approximate theory [5,6] are plotted versus distance from the nucleus in Fig. 1.1. Raimes has made recent calculations of the wave function for the 3s electrons in magnesium.[7]   The electron density plot in Fig. 1.2 was

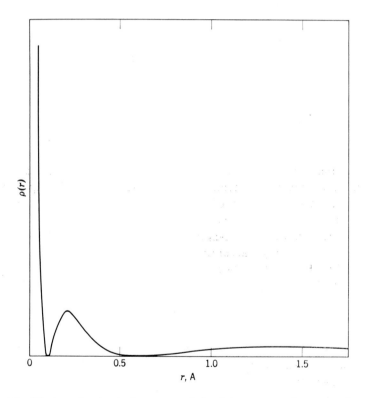

Fig. 1.2.   Electron density in 3s state as derived from magnesium wave function according to Raimes.[7]

Table 1.2.   X-ray Mass Absorption Coefficients, $\mu/\rho$, for Magnesium [8]

| $\lambda$, A | $\mu/\rho$ |
|---|---|
| 0.064 | 0.130 |
| 0.072 | 0.140 |
| 0.098 | 0.152 |
| 0.130 | 0.168 |
| 0.175 | 0.205 |
| 0.200 | 0.250 |
| 0.260 | 0.343 |
| 0.417 | 0.945 |
| 0.497 | 1.52 |
| 0.631 | 3.00 |
| 0.710 | 4.30 |
| 0.880 | 8.34 |
| 1.00 | 11.5 |
| 1.235 | 21.4 |
| 1.389 | 30.0 |
| 1.54 | 40.8 |
| 1.934 | 77.2 |
| 2.50 | 161 |

derived from some of his data.  Such calculations are useful not only for the development of atomic x-ray and electron scattering factors but also for the calculation of the cohesive energy, lattice parameter, and compressibility of the crystal.

The variation with wavelength of the mass absorption coefficients for x-rays and $\gamma$-rays according to Allen [8] is shown in Table 1.2. Hughes and Harvey [9] quote a capture cross section for slow neutrons of 0.063 barn.

## 1.2   Structural Properties

Liquid magnesium freezes to hexagonal close-packed crystal at 650°C with a density increase of approximately 4%.  The hexagonal close-packed structure, which is the only stable solid, is displayed in Fig. 1.3a.  The lattice parameters as obtained at 25°C by Busk [10, 11] from metal of the highest purity now available are as follows:

$$c = 5.199 \text{ kX}$$

$$a = 3.202 \text{ kX}$$

$$c/a = 1.624$$

A kX unit is equal to 1.002 angstrom units ($10^{-8}$ cm). If alternating *ABAB* close-packed layers were made up of perfectly hard spheres, $c/a$ would take the "ideal" value of 1.633. The actual value of $c/a$ shows that the magnesium crystal is very nearly atomically close-packed. In fact, its packing is the nearest to the ideal of any of the common hexagonal close-packed metals. The metals zinc and cad-

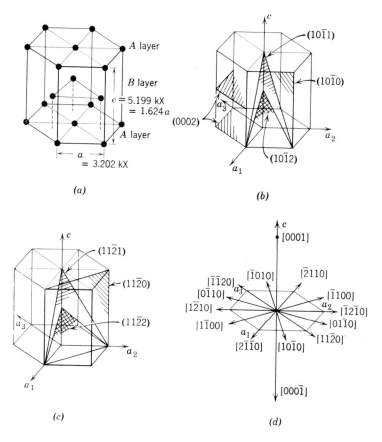

Fig. 1.3. The magnesium crystal. (*a*) Atomic positions; (*b*) principal planes of the [1$\bar{2}$10] zone; (*c*) principal planes of the [1$\bar{1}$00] zone; (*d*) principal directions.

**Table 1.3.   The Principal Atomic Planes of the Magnesium Crystal**

| {hkil} | Name | d, kX | (sin θ)/λ | Structure Factor, F | Multi-plicity |
|---|---|---|---|---|---|
| {0001} | Basal | 5.20 | 0.096 | 0 | 2 |
| {10$\bar{1}$0} | Prism, type 1 | 2.77 | 0.180 | $f$ | 6 |
| (0002) | Basal | 2.60 | 0.192 | 2$f$ | 2 |
| {10$\bar{1}$1} | Pyramidal, first order, type 1 | 2.45 | 0.204 | $\sqrt{3}\,f$ | 12 |
| {10$\bar{1}$2} | Pyramidal, second order, type 2 | 1.90 | 0.263 | $f$ | 12 |
| {11$\bar{2}$0} | Prism, type 2 | 1.60 | 0.312 | 2$f$ | 6 |
| {11$\bar{2}$1} | Pyramidal, first order, type 2 | 1.53 | 0.327 | 0 | 12 |
| {11$\bar{2}$2} | Pyramidal, second order, type 2 | 1.36 | 0.368 | 2$f$ | 12 |

mium show a large positive deviation with $c/a = 1.856$ and $1.886$. Beryllium, titanium, and zirconium have ratios on the low side at $1.585$, $1.587$, and $1.589$ respectively.

The atomic planes of hexagonal close-packed crystals are most instructively represented by the four-index system. The $(hkil)$ plane intercepts the $a_1$, $a_2$, $a_3$, and $c$ axes in Fig. 1.3$b$ at coordinates $a(1/h, 1/k, 1/i)$ and $c(1/l)$. The three-index system using $(hkl)$ and $a_1$, $a_2$, and $c$ axes only is sufficient to specify planes unambiguously. However, the four-index system has the marked advantage that all planes of the same family $\{hkil\}$ show the same numbers in the indices. The redundancy of the system is expressed by the condition that $h + k = -i$, a relation that is useful in checking notation. The principal planes of the magnesium crystal are shown in Fig. 1.3 and listed in Table 1.3, along with the variables that control the position and intensity of x-ray or electron diffraction maxima.

The interplanar distance $d$ has been calculated from the following relationship for hexagonal crystals:

$$\frac{1}{d^2} = \frac{4}{3}\frac{h^2 + hk + k^2}{a^2} + \frac{l^2}{c^2}$$

It can be seen that diffraction is not obtained from $\{0001\}$ or $\{11\bar{2}1\}$ planes.

The four-index system is also used to indicate directions within the hexagonal close-packed crystal. The direction $[hkil]$ is that defined by successive translations $ha$, $ka$, $ia$, and $lc$ parallel to the $a_1$, $a_2$, $a_3$, and $c$ axes respectively. The indices are taken as the smallest group of whole numbers which satisfy the condition that $h + k = -i$. Here also the four-index system has the advantage over the three-index system that all directions of the same family $\langle hkil \rangle$ present the same numbers in the indices. There are only three families of directions that are of high enough symmetry to be important in the crystallography of hexagonal close-packed structures. The first family is $\langle 0001 \rangle$, which are simply the positive and negative directions of the $c$ axis. They are the zone axes (directions of intersection) of the planes of the family $\{hki0\}$. The second is $\langle 11\bar{2}0 \rangle$. They are the positive and negative directions of the $a_1$, $a_2$, and $a_3$ axes and are, therefore, the atomically close-packed directions in the crystal. They are the zone axes for the planes of the families $\{10\bar{1}l\}$. The third family of directions is $\langle 10\bar{1}0 \rangle$. They are the six directions that bisect the positive and negative directions of the $a$ axes. They are the zone axes of planes of the families $\{11\bar{2}l\}$. These 14 principal directions are shown in Fig. 1.3$d$.

Precisely calculated values of the angle between planes of the magnesium crystal have been published by Salkovitz [12] and Taylor and Leber [13] from the following formula:

$$\cos \phi = \frac{h_1 h_2 + k_1 k_2 + \frac{1}{2}(h_1 k_2 + h_2 k_1) + \frac{3}{4}(a^2/c^2)l_1 l_2}{\sqrt{\left\{ \begin{array}{l} (h_1{}^2 + k_1{}^2 + h_1 k_1 + \frac{3}{4}(a^2/c^2)l_1{}^2) \\ \times (h^2 + k_2{}^2 + h_2 k_2 + \frac{3}{4}(a^2/c^2)l_2{}^2) \end{array} \right\}}}$$

The subscripts 1 and 2 refer to the two planes that meet at the angle $\phi$. Their results are summarized in Table 1.4. The stereographic projection is a much used tool in studies of pure metal crystal behavior. The (0001) standard projection according to Taylor and Leber [13] is given in Fig. 1.4 .

Six nearest neighbors at 3.19-kX distance and six second-nearest neighbors at 3.20 kX surround a magnesium atom in the crystal at 25°C. This corresponds to atomic radii of 1.595 and 1.60 kX. The atoms are relatively "open" as shown by the effective $ionic$ radius of 0.9 kX in the approximation of Zachariasen.[14] That is to say, there is relatively little overlapping of the underlying ion cores. The valence or $3s^2$ electrons contribute primarily to the metallic bonding. For this and for other reasons to be discussed in Chapter 2, the magnesium crystal is a very interesting solid from a theoretical standpoint.

The measured density of 1.738 g/cc at 25°C is identical with the value calculated by Busk from precision lattice parameters and atomic weight.[10,11] The densities of the solid and liquid magnesium at the melting point are 1.65 and 1.58, giving a density increase of 4.2%. The surface tension of liquid magnesium appears to be about

**Table 1.4.   Angles between Crystallographic Planes for Magnesium** [13]

| $(h_1k_1i_1l_1)$ | $(h_2k_2i_2l_2)$ | $\phi$ |
|---|---|---|
| 0001 | 10$\bar{1}$8 | 13.19 |
|  | 10$\bar{1}$7 | 14.99 |
|  | 10$\bar{1}$6 | 17.35 |
|  | 10$\bar{1}$5 | 20.55 |
|  | 10$\bar{1}$4 | 25.11 |
|  | 20$\bar{2}$7 | 28.17 |
|  | 10$\bar{1}$3 | 32.00 |
|  | 20$\bar{2}$5 | 36.87 |
|  | 10$\bar{1}$2 | 43.15 |
|  | 20$\bar{2}$3 | .51.31 |
|  | 10$\bar{1}$1 | 61.92 |
|  | 20$\bar{2}$1 | 75.07 |
|  | 10$\bar{1}$0 | 90.00 |
|  | 21$\bar{3}$2 | 68.04 |
|  | 21$\bar{3}$1 | 78.60 |
|  | 21$\bar{3}$0 | 90.00 |
|  | 11$\bar{2}$8 | 22.09 |
|  | 11$\bar{2}$6 | 28.42 |
|  | 11$\bar{2}$4 | 39.07 |
|  | 11$\bar{2}$2 | 58.37 |
|  | 11$\bar{2}$0 | 90.00 |
| 10$\bar{1}$0 | 21$\bar{3}$0 | 19.11 |
|  | 11$\bar{2}$0 | 30.00 |
|  | 01$\bar{1}$0 | 60.00 |

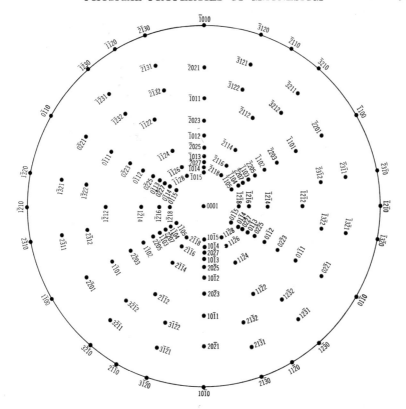

Fig. 1.4.  (0001) standard projection for magnesium.[13]

600 ergs/cm², and its viscosity near the melting point is 12.3–12.5 millipoises.[15]

The vapor pressure of solid magnesium above 500°C is great enough to allow the formation of sublimation pits.  The striking crystallographically oriented development of these pits has been reported by Grall.[16]

## 1.3   Thermal, Electrical, and Magnetic Properties

The heat capacity, enthalpy, and entropy of magnesium at temperatures above 298°K are presented in Table 1.5.  These data were gathered by Stull and Sinke from several sources and represent the best averaged values now available.[17]  The heat of fusion has been

Table 1.5.  Thermodynamic Properties of Magnesium [17, 19]

| $T$ Temperature, °K | $C_p^0$ Heat Capacity, cal/deg/mole | $H_t^0 - H_{298.16}^0$ Heat Content, cal/mole | $S_t^0$ Entropy, cal/deg/mole | $P_0$, mm of Hg |
|---|---|---|---|---|
| 298.16 | 5.93 | | 7.77 | |
| 300 | 5.94 | 10 | 7.81 | |
| 400 | 6.29 | 622 | 9.57 | |
| 500 | 6.58 | 1266 | 11.00 | |
| 600 | 6.84 | 1938 | 12.23 | |
| 700 | 7.09 | 2634 | 13.30 | |
| 750 | 7.24 | | | |
| 800 | 7.42 | 3359 | 14.27 | |
| 850 | 7.61 | | | |
| 900 | 7.81 | 4120 | 15.16 | 1.2 |
| 950 | 7.75 | | | 3.5 |
| 1000 | 7.88 | 7040 | 18.31 | 8 |
| 1050 | 8.01 | | | 17 |
| 1100 | 8.14 | 7841 | 19.07 | 34 |
| 1150 | | | | 66 |
| 1200 | 8.40 | 8668 | 19.79 | 128 |
| 1250 | | | | 230 |
| 1300 | 8.66 | 9521 | 20.47 | 380 |
| 1350 | | | | 600 |
| 1400 | 4.97 | 42321 | 44.26 | |
| 1500 | 4.97 | 42818 | 44.60 | |
| 1600 | 4.97 | 43315 | 44.92 | |
| 1700 | 4.97 | 43812 | 45.22 | |
| 1800 | 4.97 | 44308 | 45.50 | |
| 1900 | 4.97 | 44805 | 45.77 | |
| 2000 | 4.97 | 45302 | 46.03 | |
| 2100 | 4.97 | 45799 | 46.27 | |
| 2200 | 4.97 | 46295 | 46.50 | |
| 2300 | 4.97 | 46792 | 46.72 | |
| 2400 | 4.97 | 47289 | 46.93 | |
| 2500 | 4.97 | 47785 | 47.14 | |
| 2600 | 4.97 | 48282 | 47.33 | |
| 2700 | 4.97 | 48779 | 47.52 | |
| 2800 | 4.97 | 49276 | 47.70 | |
| 2900 | 4.97 | 49772 | 47.87 | |
| 3000 | 4.97 | 50269 | 48.04 | |

measured at 2140 cal/g-atom.[18]  Stull has also made a critical evaluation of published values of the vapor pressure of magnesium and values interpolated from his summary [19] are included in Table 1.5.  They extrapolate to a normal boiling point of 1380°K (1107°C).  Stull and Sinke have calculated a heat of vaporization of 32.0 ± 0.5 kcal/g-atom, assuming the gas to be ideally monatomic.

The Debye characteristic temperature $\theta$ has been found by Smith [20] to be constant at 326° at all temperatures above 30°K, and to increase to 406 ± 10°K at absolute zero.  Logan, Clement, and Jeffers [21] and Slutsky and Garland [22] have reported values of $\theta$ at absolute zero of 390°K and 388 ± 3°K respectively.

An analysis of 13 published investigations of the thermal expansion of magnesium by Baker [23] has led to the following best fitting relation for the temperature range 0–550°C:

$$\alpha_t = 25.0 + 0.0188t$$

where $\alpha_t$ is in units of $10^{-6}/°C$ and $t$ is in °C.  Length changes for pure magnesium may be obtained with fair accuracy by the integration of this relation as follows:

$$l_{t_2} = l_{t_1}\left(1 + \int_{t_1}^{t_2} \alpha_t \, dt\right) = l_0[1 + (25.0t + 0.0094t^2)]$$

The electrical resistivity of pure magnesium as a function of temperature is plotted in Fig. 1.5.  The values for the solid range were chosen from a survey of 13 publications.[23]  The latest and perhaps the best values of resistivity and temperature coefficient of resistivity at 20°C as reported by Salkovitz, Schindler, and Kammer,[24] $4.450 \times 10^{-6}$ ohm-cm and $1.656 \times 10^{-8}$ ohm-cm/°C, agree well with this summary plot.  The resistivity appears not to be a linear function of temperature at any point in the range shown.  The positive deviation from linearity increases as the melting point is approached.  Resistivity minima in solid magnesium of various purities have been observed at temperatures of a few degrees absolute.[25-28]  Such minima have been reported for several metals and, although the effect is thought to be associated with impurities, it is not well understood at present.  The small negative temperature coefficient shown in the liquid range of Fig. 1.5 results from acceptance of the value of Scala and Robertson,[29] who found such behavior in several molten metals.

The magnesium single crystal shows anisotropy of electrical resistivity.  The most complete data of the orientation effect were summarized by Nichols [30] in the relation:

$$\rho(\phi) = 4.60 - 0.75 \cos^2 \phi$$

where $\phi$ is the angle between the hexagonal axis and the direction of current flow, and $\rho$ is the resistivity in microhm-cm. The resistivity is rotationally symmetrical about the hexagonal axis. Nichols obtained temperature coefficients of resistivity of $3.90 \times 10^{-3}$ and $4.08 \times 10^{-3}/°C$ in the directions perpendicular and parallel to the hexagonal axis respectively, for the temperature range 24–200°C. The electrical resistivity of a polycrystalline aggregate of magnesium will be noticeably dependent on its degree of preferred orientation.

The Hall constant at 20°C for highest purity magnesium is $-8.42 \times 10^{-13}$ ohm-cm/oersted.[24] Its thermoelectric power is $-0.222$ at 300°K and $-0.142$ at 78°K.[24]

Thermal conductivity of magnesium has not been measured with any degree of accuracy. However, comparison of measurements of

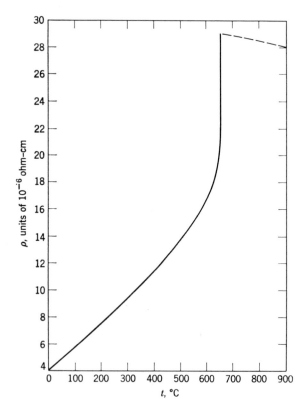

Fig. 1.5. Electrical resistivity of magnesium as a function of temperature.

thermal and electrical conductivities of many magnesium alloys show that the Wiedemann-Franz Law holds to a close approximation. This relation is classically expressed in the form

$$L = \frac{K}{\sigma T}$$

where $L$ is the Lorentz function (a constant when the law holds), $K$ is the thermal conductivity, $\sigma$ is the electrical conductivity, and $T$ is the absolute temperature. Powell reached the conclusion that, if 0.57 is taken as the value of $L$, the thermal conductivities of magnesium and its alloys should be derivable to 5% accuracy.[31] He gives the following relation as the best fit of his data from a rather unusual group of alloys:

$$K = 0.516 \times 10^{-8}\sigma T + 0.022$$

where $K$ is in g-cal/cm-sec-°K and $\sigma$ is in (ohm-cm)$^{-1}$. Bungardt and Kallenbach [32] present the following analogous relation:

$$\frac{K}{T} = 0.54 \times 10^{-8}\sigma + 0.4 \times 10^{-4}$$

**Table 1.6. Calculation of Thermal Conductivity from the Electrical Conductivity of Magnesium**

| Temperature, °K | Electrical Conductivity, $10^5$ (ohm-cm)$^{-1}$ | Thermal Conductivity, g-cal/cm-sec-°K | |
|---|---|---|---|
| | | Powell Equation [31] | Bungardt and Kallenbach [32] Equation |
| 273 | 2.43 | 0.364 | 0.37 |
| 293 | 2.24 | 0.361 | 0.37 |
| 323 | 2.01 | 0.358 | 0.36 |
| 373 | 1.71 | 0.351 | 0.36 |
| 423 | 1.48 | 0.346 | 0.36 |
| 473 | 1.32 | 0.343 | 0.36 |
| 523 | 1.16 | 0.337 | 0.35 |
| 573 | 1.05 | 0.333 | 0.35 |
| 623 | 0.95 | 0.328 | 0.34 |
| 673 | 0.86 | 0.321 | 0.34 |

Table 1.6 shows some electrical conductivity values corresponding to Fig. 1.5 and thermal conductivities calculated from each of the relations above. It appears that one may use the value of 0.36 for the $K$ of magnesium over the range 0–200°C with probability of very small error.

Magnesium is paramagnetic with a mass susceptibility of $0.50 \times 10^{-6}$ cgs units according to Gaber.[33] The diamagnetic mass susceptibility of the $Mg^{++}$ ion has been measured as $-0.18 \times 10^{-6}$. This part of the susceptibility is in good agreement with the theoretical value of $-0.17 \times 10^{-6}$ obtained by Hartree. The conduction electrons add both a paramagnetic and a diamagnetic component to the total susceptibility. Calculation using the formula of Landau[34] based on the free-electron theory leads to a diamagnetic component of $-0.19 \times 10^{-6}$. Since free electrons give a paramagnetic component resulting from their spin which is just three times this diamagnetic component, the resultant theoretical free-electron susceptibility is $0.38 \times 10^{-6}$. The difference between the measured values for the metal and the ion, $0.68 \times 10^{-6}$, is nearly twice the theoretical value of free-electron susceptibility. This discrepancy probably results from the nearly overlapped Brillouin zone for magnesium.

# References

1. R. K. Sheline and N. R. Johnson, "New Long Lived $Mg^{28}$ Isotope," *Phys. Rev.*, **89**, 520 (1953).
2. J. W. Jones and T. P. Kohman, "Synchrocyclotron Production and Properties of $Mg^{28}$," *Phys. Rev.*, **90**, 495 (1953).
3. R. W. James and G. W. Brindley, "Some Numerical Calculations of Atomic Scattering Factors," *Phil. Mag.*, **12**, 104 (1931).
4. D. R. Hartree, "The Wave Mechanics of an Atom with a Non-Coulomb Central Field," *Proc. Cambridge Phil. Soc.*, **24**, 89, 111 (1928).
5. L. H. Thomas, "The Calculation of Atomic Fields," *Proc. Cambridge Phil. Soc.*, **23**, 542 (1927).
6. E. Fermi, "Eine statistiche Methode zur Bestimmung einiger Eigenschaften des Atoms und ihre Anwendung auf die Theorie des periodischen Systems der Elemente," *Z. Physik*, **48**, 73 (1928).
7. S. Raimes, "Cohesive Energy of Metallic Magnesium," *Phil. Mag.*, **41**, 568 (1950).
8. S. J. M. Allen, in A. H. Compton and S. K. Allison, *X-rays in Theory and Experiment*, D. Van Nostrand, Princeton, N. J., 1935, p. 800.
9. D. J. Hughes and J. A. Harvey, *Neutron Cross Sections*, U. S. Government Printing Office, Washington, 1955.

10. R. S. Busk, "Lattice Parameters of Magnesium Alloys," *Trans. AIME*, **188**, 1460 (1952).
11. R. S. Busk, "Effect of Temperature on the Lattice Parameters of Magnesium Alloys," *Trans. AIME*, **194**, 207 (1952).
12. E. I. Salkovitz, "Crystallographic Angles for Magnesium, Zinc and Cadmium," *Trans. AIME*, **191**, 64 and 880 (1951).
13. A. Taylor and S. Leber, "Crystallographic Angles for Hexagonal Metals," *Trans. AIME*, **200**, 190 (1954).
14. W. H. Zachariasen, "A Set of Empirical Crystal Radii for Ions With Inert Gas Configurations," *Z. Krist.*, **80**, 137 (1931).
15. M. F. Culpin, "The Viscosity of Liquid Magnesium and Liquid Calcium," *Proc. Phys. Soc. (London)*, **70**, 1079 (1957).
16. L. Grall, "Formation and Advantages of Orientated Structures Obtained by Sublimation on Magnesium," *Rev. mét.*, **52**, 603 (1955).
17. D. R. Stull and G. C. Sinke, *Thermodynamic Properties of the Elements*, Advance in Chemistry Series, No. 18, American Chemical Society, Washington, 1956, 124.
18. D. R. Stull and R. A. McDonald, "The Enthalpy and Heat Capacity of Magnesium and Type 430 Stainless Steel from 700 to 1100°K," *J. Am. Chem. Soc.*, **77**, 5293 (1955).
19. D. R. Stull, "Vapor Pressure of Pure Substances," *Ind. Eng. Chem.*, **39**, 543 (1947).
20. P. L. Smith, "The Specific Heats of Magnesium and Zinc," *Phil. Mag.*, **46**, 744 (1955).
21. J. K. Logan, J. R. Clement, and H. R. Jeffers, "Resistance Minimum of Magnesium: Heat Capacity between 3°K and 13°K," *Phys. Rev.*, **105**, 1435 (1957).
22. L. J. Slutsky and C. W. Garland, "Elastic Constants of Magnesium from 4.2°K to 300°K," *Phys. Rev.*, **107**, 972 (1957).
23. H. Baker (unpublished report), The Dow Chemical Company, Midland, Mich., 1957.
24. E. I. Salkovitz, A. J. Schindler, and F. W. Kammer, "Transport Properties of Dilute Binary Magnesium Alloys," *Phys. Rev.*, **105**, 887 (1957).
25. J. G. Thomas and E. Mendoza, "The Electrical Resistance of Magnesium, Aluminum, Molybdenum, Cobalt and Tungsten at Low Temperatures," *Phil. Mag.*, **43**, 900 (1952).
26. W. R. G. Kemp, A. K. Sreedhar, and G. K. White, "The Thermal Conductivity of Magnesium at Low Temperatures," *Proc. Phys. Soc. (London)*, **66**, 1077 (1953).
27. H. M. Rosenberg, "The Thermal and Electrical Conductivity of Magnesium at Low Temperatures," *Phil. Mag.*, **45**, 13 (1954).
28. D. A. Spohr and R. T. Webber, "Resistance Minimum of Magnesium: Electrical and Thermal Resistivities," *Phys. Rev.*, **105**, 1427 (1957).
29. E. Scala and W. D. Robertson, "Electrical Resistivity of Liquid Metals and of Dilute Liquid Metallic Solutions," *Trans. AIME*, **197**, 1141 (1953).
30. J. L. Nichols, "Orientation and Temperature Effects on the Electrical Resistivity of High-Purity Magnesium," *J. Appl. Phys.*, **26**, 471 (1955).
31. R. W. Powell, "The Thermal and Electrical Conductivities of Some Magnesium Alloys," *Phil. Mag.*, **27**, 677 (1939).

32. W. Bungardt and R. Kallenbach, "Über den Zusammenhang zwischen der thermischen und elektrischen Leitfähigkeit bei Aluminium und Magnesium-Legierungen," *Metall,* **4,** 317, 365 (1950).

33. M. Gaber (unpublished result), Michigan State University, East Lansing, Mich., 1958.

34. L. Landau, "Diamagnetismus der Metalle," *Z. Physik,* **64,** 629 (1930).

# 2

# Alloy Theory
# and
# Properties

The pure metal magnesium is not valuable in many technological applications. As in the engineering of other metals, alloying of magnesium has been used to obtain strength, ductility, workability, corrosion resistance, low density, and castability. This chapter introduces the theory available to explain solubility range and structure of the various phases as well as the equilibrium between them. The equilibria themselves are summarized in the diagrams of Chapter 3.

Two alloy theories are important in the science of magnesium. One is semiempirical, correlating the structure, and extent of solubility of phases with such directly measurable properties as the atomic size, effective valence, and chemical activity of the constituent metals. The second group of theories is based on the semiquantitative application of quantum mechanics to the behavior of various possible or actual crystal structures in the system under consideration.

The two theories are complementary in their application to magnesium. However, it is convenient to treat them somewhat separately in the following two sections.

## 2.1 The Empirical Theory of Magnesium Alloys

Several factors influence the extent of solid solubility of one metal in another. In the first place, there cannot be complete solid solubility in a binary system unless the components both have the same crystal structure. Even if the structure is the same, the factors of atomic size, chemical affinity, and electron concentration appear to control the extent of solubility. Hume-Rothery has shown that, if the atomic radii of two elements differ by more than 15%, extensive solid

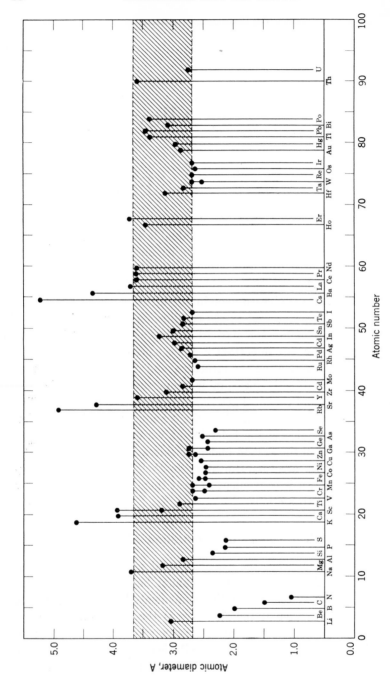

Fig. 2.1.  Atomic diameters of the elements and favorable size-factor zone with respect to magnesium.[2]

solubility may not be expected.[1]  If the two components have a
chemical attraction, i.e., if one of them is electronegative and the other
is electropositive, intermetallic compounds are favored over continuous
solid solubility.  Finally, as discussed in Section 2.2, if the Fermi
energy of the electrons becomes an important factor, phase changes
may be introduced into the equilibrium because of Brillouin zone
overlap.

    An analysis of the relative effects of the size factor in the alloying
of magnesium has been presented by Carapella.[2]  The atoms whose

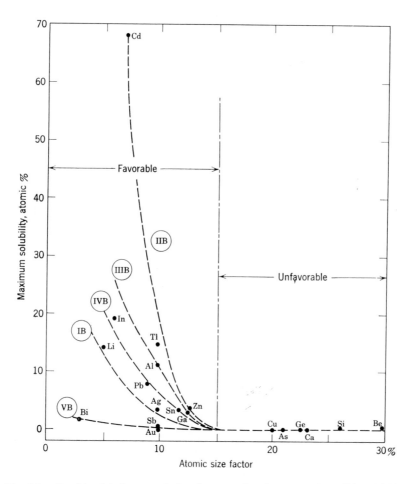

Fig. 2.2.  Combined influence of size factor and valence on the solid solubility
of B group metals in magnesium.[2]

sizes place them within the favorable $\pm 15\%$ range with respect to magnesium are shown within the shaded band of Fig. 2.1. The "atomic diameters" used for such a plot may be determined in several ways, but the difference in results for a given element is generally less than the accuracy of the empirical theory. With an atomic diameter of 3.20 A, magnesium is in a central position where the favorable size-factor range covers many other atomic species. As a result, extensive solid solubility might be expected in many magnesium-based binary

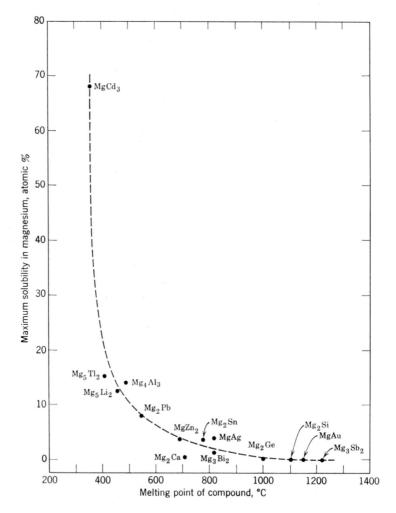

Fig. 2.3.   Influence of compound stability on maximum solid-solubility.[2]

systems. The other factors of valence and chemical affinity prove to be severe limitations, however.

The *valence effect* is the reduced tendency for extensive solid solution formation when the alloying element differs from that of the solvent. The *electrochemical effect* is the tendency to form a stable intermetallic phase and, thus, to restrict the extent of solid solubility when the solute atom is much more electropositive or electronegative than the solvent.

The size-factor and valency effects for magnesium are summarized in Fig. 2.2. The maximum solubility occurs in the series of solutes from group IIB of the periodic table, in agreement with the valency effect. The solubility decreases with increasing size factor until the approximate 15% level, beyond which the solubility is negligible.

Correlations between the stability of intermetallic compounds, as represented by melting point, and the extent of solid solubility are evidence of the operation of an electrochemical effect. The correlation is shown for a large number of group B solutes in Fig. 2.3.

Carapella has drawn some practical conclusions for the designer of commercial alloys from his analysis of the empirical alloy theory of magnesium. They are as follows:

1. A favorable size factor influences both the liquidus and solidus curves, leading to a narrower freezing range. This is desirable for the design of a casting alloy. This correlation may be seen in the diagrams of Chapter 3, by contrasting the freezing range in the Mg-Tl system, where the size factor is only 7% with those in the Mg-Al, Mg-Ga, and Mg-Zn systems, the size factors of which are $-10\%$, $-24\%$, and $-17\%$ respectively.

2. When the solubility is strongly controlled by the size factor, the solid solubility generally increases with increasing temperature. Such a variation is a necessary, although not a sufficient, condition for precipitation hardening. Thus the designer of new age-hardenable systems may refer profitably to the size-factor effect as a preliminary guide to success.

More information on the influence of the atomic or ionic size factor is presented and discussed in Section 2.3.

## 2.2  Electron Theories of Magnesium

The majority of the calculations for the magnesium crystal have been made with the so-called nearly free-electron approximation leading to what is called the Brillouin zone theory. A large amount of work was done with this approach by Jones,[3-5] who considered the electronic structure of not only magnesium but also of several alloy phases which exhibited nearly close-packed hexagonal structure. The Brillouin zone theory for magnesium regards all but the 3s electrons as bound, and solves for the one-electron wave functions of the 3s electrons on the assumption that they are moving in the periodic potential energy field of the ion cores and the smeared "self-consistent" field of those electrons themselves. The mathematics involve the use of standard perturbation theory to modify the plane-wave functions which would apply if the electrons were completely free in space. The theory is explained in both qualitative and quantitative terms in several texts.[6-10]

The success of the Brillouin zone theory in explaining some aspects of the behavior of magnesium and its alloys depends on the singularities associated with electron overlaps of the zones. However, before these correlations are discussed, a very important qualification must be emphasized. More recent theoretical effort in solid state physics has shown that, in principle, the nearly free-electron approximation must be so far from representing the actual state of affairs as to be theoretically useless for describing real crystals. It has been found that the modifications of the plane-wave functions by standard perturbation theory are quite unacceptable when the real potential field of crystals is examined. The modern methods of the orthogonalized plane wave, the augmented plane wave, and combinations thereof are found to be far better approximations to the truth than the nearly free-electron approximation.[11] These later methods utilize the self-consistent field also, but resort to much more complicated mathematics to represent the perturbation of the electronic wave functions by the periodic potential of the crystal structure. However, the Brillouin zone theory seems to give rather correct answers in spite of its poor basis, owing to the superficial similarity which its results bear to those of the better approximations. The augmented plane-wave method in one of its earlier forms has been applied to magnesium by Trlifaj.[12]

Other investigators [13-15] have refined the concepts of Brillouin-zone–Fermi-surface interaction in hexagonal crystals first introduced by Jones. Although they disagree with his postulated mechanism in some cases, they obtain results which are in general qualitative agreement with his.

The first zone for this nearly close-packed hexagonal crystal is shown in Fig. 2.4a. As may be expected from the diffraction spectrum, it is

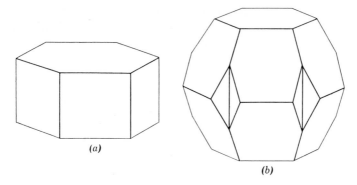

Fig. 2.4. (*a*) First and (*b*) second Brillouin zones for hexagonal close-packed crystal.

defined by the equivalent in reciprocal space of the $\{10\bar{1}0\}$ and $\{0001\}$ planes. This zone contains only one energy state for electrons per atom, because the primitive cell of the crystal contains two atoms rather than one, as in the cubic metals. In addition, this zone has no energy discontinuities across the top and bottom planes. This corresponds to the lack of x-ray diffraction from the $\{0001\}$ planes ($F = 0$ in Table 1.3) in the magnesium crystal. The second Brillouin zone is bounded everywhere by planes of energy discontinuity and is presented in Fig. 2.4*b*. This rather complicated surface is defined by the reciprocal space equivalents to the $\{0002\}$, $\{10\bar{1}1\}$, and $\{10\bar{1}0\}$ planes. In addition to the exterior planes of energy discontinuity, which are visible in Fig. 2.4*b*, surfaces of energy discontinuity of the equivalent form $\{10\bar{1}0\}$ exist around the equatorial section of the zone. These planes are seen in Fig. 2.5 which shows a composite zone made up of the first and part of the second zone. This zone for magnesium contains 1.74 electron states per atom of the real crystal. The energy function discontinuities of particular importance in the following discussion are those across the

Fig. 2.5. Composite zone for the hexagonal close-packed crystal.

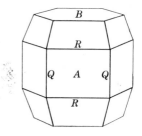

prism or $A$ faces and those across the basal or $B$ faces of the zone. No energy discontinuity occurs across the edges $Q$ or $R$ until the triangular prisms, which complete the second zone of Fig. 2.4$b$, are added.

As the electronic states within the zone are filled, the Fermi surface eventually touches a plane of energy discontinuity, and, by definition, overlap occurs. The proportions of the magnesium zone are such that, if a spherical Fermi surface is assumed, as would be proper only for completely free electrons, the overlaps of filling of states in the next zone occur first across the middle of the $A$ faces of the composite zone into the remainder of the complete second zone. As more states are filled, the next overlap of a spherical surface would be across the edges $Q$ into the third Brillouin zone. The third overlap would occur across the mid-points of the basal faces $B$ into the third zone also. Thus the order of overlap is given as $AQB$. With an electron-to-atom ratio of exactly two, as in pure magnesium, the $A$ and $Q$ overlaps have occurred but the $B$ overlap has not.

In contrast to magnesium are zinc and cadmium, where the overlaps are in the order $BAQ$. This is easily understood in terms of the high $c/a$ ratios for these crystals. Because of the reciprocal property of $k$ space, a tall unit cell of high $c/a$ ratio in the real crystal corresponds to a short, squat Brillouin zone in reciprocal space, and vice versa. Thus, for zinc and cadmium, the shortness of the zone leads to a contact of the nearly spherical Fermi surface first with the bases, then with the sides, and finally with the corners, giving the order of overlap $BAQ$.

The density-of-states curve is the immediate end result of the calculations, whether they have been made by the free-electron approximation or by the more modern methods. A qualitative representation of the density of states for magnesium, showing the sequence of over-

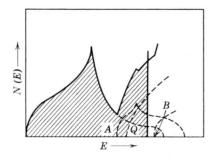

Fig. 2.6. Qualitative density of electronic states as constructed by Mott.

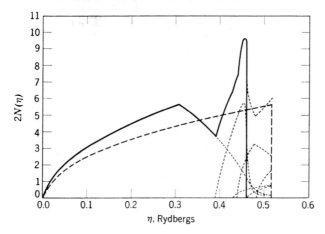

Fig. 2.7. Density of electronic states for magnesium as calculated by Trlifaj.[12] The curve drawn in full represents the actual distribution of the density of the valence electrons. The dashed line corresponds to the density of free electrons.

laps, Fig. 2.6, was made by Mott.* The recent calculations of Trlifaj [12] have led to the development of a quantitatively significant density of states, Fig. 2.7. The larger number of segments being added to give the resulting curve is another manifestation of the greater complexity of the more accurate theories as compared to the simple Brillouin zone theory. Another important difference is the lack of coincidence of the curve with the free-electron parabola even at the low-energy end. This difference results from one of the most elementary refinements of the simple zone theory, namely, the use of an effective electronic mass which is different from the normal value that would apply to a completely free electron.

The theoretical density-of-states curve can be checked experimentally with some degree of precision by measurements of the soft (long wavelength) x-ray emission spectrum of the solid in question. Such measurements have been made by Skinner [16] and Cady and Tomboulian,[17] whose results are shown in Fig. 2.8. As might be expected, they are both in better agreement with the curve of Trlifaj than with the schematic curve of Mott. The greatest difference is that of shape between the maxima and before the $A$ overlap. The nearly free-electron approximation predicts a very sharp decrease in the density

* First published in Reference 1.

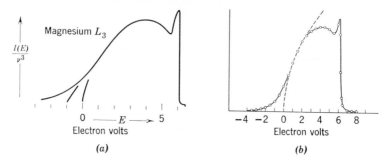

Fig. 2.8. *L*-emission curves for magnesium (*a*) by Skinner [16] and (*b*) by Cady and Tomboulian.[17]

of states once the Fermi surface touches the zone boundaries, whereas the more accurate approximation predicts a much more gradual decrease, as is found in the emission spectra.

## 2.3    Binary Solid Solubility and Lattice Parameters

Let us consider first the lattice parameter and axial ratio variations as we replace magnesium atoms in the hexagonal close-packed structure with solute atoms. The effective valence or electron concentration effect and the ionic size effect are sufficiently separable that general relations may be written for lattice parameters of many binary systems. Such relations have been found experimentally, analyzed statistically, and presented in very useful form by Busk.[18] Indeed, he has found that the relations are general enough to be useful in many ternary solid solutions of magnesium.

It is appropriate to review the first work on the subject. Raynor and Hume-Rothery [19–21] presented the variations in the *c* and *a* parameters and the axial ratio *c/a* as a function of atomic percent of various solutes of valence from one to four. The results were interpretable in terms of the Brillouin zone theory as it has been developed by Jones. They found that the alloying of monovalent and divalent metals in the magnesium solid solution caused the normal smooth changes in the lattice parameters that one might expect simply from atomic size effects. However, when trivalent and tetravalent atoms, such as gallium, indium, lead, and tin, were added to the magnesium solid solution, discontinuities in slope were found in the plots of *c* parameter versus composition. These sharp changes in slope occurred at atomic concen-

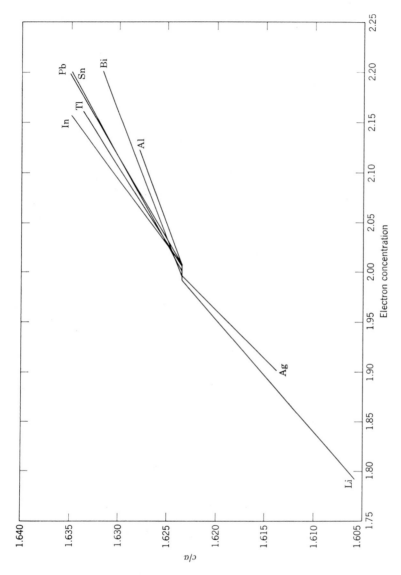

Fig. 2.9. Axial ratio $c/a$ of magnesium binary alloys as a function of electron concentration.[18]

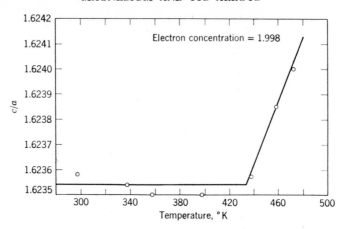

Fig. 2.10.  Variation with temperature of the $c/a$ ratio of Mg-0.18% Ag alloy.[22]

trations or electron-to-atom ratios that corresponded quite well with the anticipated electron concentration at which one would expect the B overlap in the Brillouin zone for magnesium.  This effect is shown in Fig. 2.9.  Here the $c/a$ ratio is taken as the most significant variable in assessing the effect of changing electron concentration.

The effect of increasing temperature on $c/a$ was also studied.[22]  This ratio remains constant until the combined effect of the temperature increase and the alloying addition caused a sharp rise.  The simple zone theory predicts such an effect because temperature increase causes an expansion of the unit cell in the real crystal.  This corresponds to a shrinkage of the Brillouin zone volume in reciprocal space and the occurrence once again of a B overlap.  This is illustrated by the data for a dilute Mg-Ag alloy in Fig. 2.10.  The quantitative expression of Busk's results take the following form.

Two groups of alloying elements were studied, those having a significant solubility range in magnesium and those having a very small solubility.  The first group include predominantly group B elements:

Li, Al, Zn, Ga, Ag, Cd, In, Sn, Tl, Hg, Pb, and Bi

The change of $c/a$ for these elements was taken as a measure of their effective valence in determining the electron concentration.  The lines in Fig. 2.9 may be represented by the equations:

$$c/a = 1.47298 + 0.07554E' \qquad E' \lessgtr 1.994$$

$$c/a = 1.62364 \qquad\qquad\qquad 1.994 \lessgtr E' \lessgtr 2.005$$

$$c/a = 1.47567 + 0.0738E' \qquad E' \geq 2.005$$

where the electron concentration $E'$ is calculable from the effective valences in Table 2.1. As can be seen, the valence derived from the data in this way is relative to an arbitrary assumption of an effective valence of 3.00 for In, the element which gives the largest slope in Fig. 2.9. If one accepts the Jones theory for magnesium, the range of $E'$ shown above where $c/a$ is constant is that in which the B overlap is taking place.

Recent measurements by D. Hardie and R. N. Parkins, *Phil. Mag.*, **4**, 815 (1959), of the lattice parameters of the binary solid solutions

Table 2.1.  **Summary of Busk's Data for Magnesium-Based Binary Alloys** [18]

| Elements | Effective Radius, (kX units) | Effective * Valence |
|---|---|---|
| Silver | 1.33 | 0.66 |
| Aluminum | 1.40 | 2.49 |
| Bismuth | 1.69 | 3.50 |
| Cadmium | 1.49 | 2.00 |
| Gallium | 1.42 | 2.00 |
| Mercury | 1.39 | 2.00 |
| Indium | 1.54 | 3.00 |
| Lithium | 1.55 | 0.84 |
| Lead | 1.64 | 3.55 |
| Tin | 1.57 | 3.50 |
| Thallium | 1.56 | 2.87 |
| Zinc | 1.37 | 2.00 |
| Magnesium | 1.60 | 2.00 |

* Relative for In = 3.00.

in magnesium of Al, Bi, Cd, In, Pb, Li, Ag, Sn, and Zn are in some disagreement with those of Busk. These authors report the following continuous linear relationship between the axial ratios and the electron concentration $E$ based on the *normal group* valences for the solutes:

$$c/a = 1.50319 + 0.060085E$$

However, some improvement in the agreement with this relation results from using the value 2.7 electrons/atom for the valence of aluminum. These results agree with the earlier and more limited studies by F. W. Von Batchelder and R. F. Raeuchle, *Phys. Rev.,* **105,** 59 (1957). Hardie and Parkins have discussed the lack of harmony of their results with the Brillouin zone overlap picture as presented here.

Busk made the reasonable assumption that the variation of the $a$ parameters in the binary solid solutions resulted from the difference in atomic size of the solute atoms and magnesium. The resulting values of $R$, the effective radius, are also given in Table 2.1. The following over-all equation can be written for the variation of $a$ with concentration in terms of these radii:

$$a = 3.20268 - (-0.032044 + 0.020014R)x$$

where $x$ is atomic percent and $a$ is in kX units. All of the results above were corrected to 25°C.

Although it was not possible to study the addition of the *slightly soluble elements* in the same complete manner, because of the extremely small lattice parameter changes involved, the statistical treatment allowed statements about the direction of parameter change. These elements are nearly all group A, transition, or rare earth elements. The following slightly soluble elements decrease $a$:

Au, Mn, Rh, and Zr

The following increase $a$:

As, Ba, Ce, La, Ni, and Pd

The following decrease $c/a$:

Au, Ce, and Pd

The following increase $c/a$:

Ba, Ir, Rh, Pt, Ti, and Zr

The remaining slightly soluble elements that were studied, Ca, Cu, Sb, Si, Te, and W, show no changes of either $a$ or $c/a$ according to statistical test applied to the data.

In his conclusions, Busk pointed out that few, if any, solutes in magnesium appear to be fully ionized (see Table 2.1). This also is in general agreement with the English investigators.[21] He also studied the lattice parameters of a group of ternary alloys and found that the values calculated from the equations and those measured agreed within the experimental error.

The effect of increasing temperature on the $c/a$ ratio of alloys that are near but not in the B overlap at room temperature also was examined. The lattice parameters were measured by the same precision technique which was used on the work described above. Alloys in the binary systems Mg-Ag, Mg-Al, and Mg-Sn as well as pure magnesium itself were used. The variation with electron concentration of the "breaking point" in the $c/a$ versus temperature curve (for example, Fig. 2.10) is plotted in Fig. 2.11. This threshold value of electron concentration which is apparently a single-valued function of the absolute temperature, as Fig. 2.11 indicates, is in itself a very striking support of the simple Brillouin zone theory of magnesium.

A study of the lattice parameter changes with composition in the binary system Mg-Cd offers the possibility of observing the influence of the change of Brillouin zone geometry on the overlap of electrons *at constant electron concentration*. As cadmium is added to magnesium, it is to be expected on the basis of the zone theory that at some

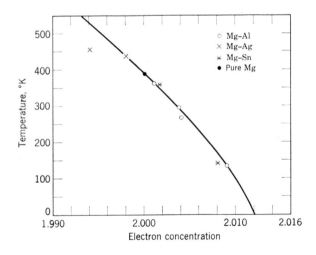

Fig. 2.11. Effect of electron concentration on the temperature at which the $c/a$ ratio for magnesium-based alloy begins to increase.[22]

concentration the Q overlap, which has occurred in magnesium and which has not in elemental cadmium, will disappear and the B overlap, which has not occurred in magnesium but which has in cadmium, will enter. Since the cadmium atom is smaller than the magnesium atom,

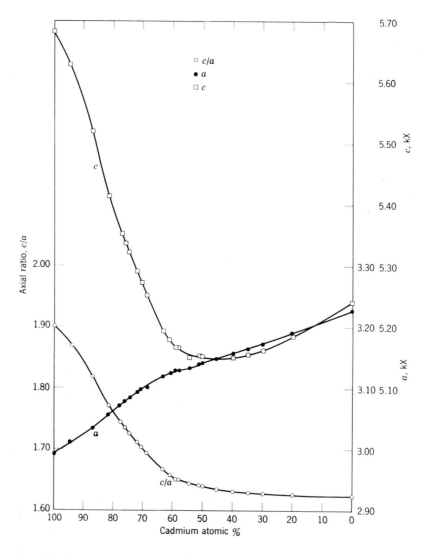

Fig. 2.12. Lattice parameters $a$ and $c$, and axial ratio $c/a$ for the Mg-Cd system at 310°C.[23]

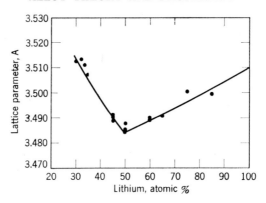

Fig. 2.13. Minimum in lattice parameter versus composition of Mg-Li alloys.[24]

one would expect that initially both $a$ and $c$ parameters would decrease with increasing cadmium content until the point at which the overlap interchange becomes appreciable. It would be expected that from then on the $a$ parameter would decrease more rapidly, and the $c$ parameter would reverse and increase rapidly to the high value characteristic of cadmium. Lattice parameters for the system from the work of Hume-Rothery and Raynor are presented in Fig. 2.12.[23] The very recognizable change in slope of the curves for the two parameters confirms the qualitative ideas of the zone theory. Of course, it is recognized that the theory is an especially great oversimplification of the situation for concentrated solid solutions of this sort, since the electronic wave functions must be much more complicated than in the dilute case. Nevertheless, the agreement does indicate the value of such a simple theory to allow prediction of the alloy behavior of magnesium.

The body-centered cubic solid solution extends well into the magnesium-rich side of the Mg-Li system. The lattice parameter variation with concentration in this phase adds supporting evidence for the usefulness of the Brillouin zone theory. It was known from Jones' original calculations that the first overlap in the $bcc$ structure should occur at an electron concentration of 1.48. The sharp change in slope at this point in the lattice parameter data obtained by Levinson [24] is apparent in Fig. 2.13.

One may expect electron transport properties to be influenced singularly by Brillouin zone overlap as dilute solid solution alloying progresses in magnesium. Extrema have been observed in the curves of

Hall coefficient and thermoelectric power versus content of trivalent and quadrivalent solute.[25, 26] These extrema have been associated with the occurrence of Brillouin zone overlap. The addition of monovalent and divalent solutes leads to a monotonic variation of the sensitive electronic transport properties. Salkovitz, Schindler, and Kammer separate the Hall coefficient and the thermoelectric power into two parts. One is thought of as being a linear contribution by the electron concentration. The other takes care of everything else, especially the disturbance in the ion-core field resulting from the presence of the solute atoms in the crystal. These authors evaluate the latter from a study of the magnesium-cadmium system. The electron-concentration-dependent term is then obtained by subtraction from the measured values. These results offer another confirmation of the usefulness of the simple Brillouin zone theory.

This work also showed that Matthiesen's rule and Linde's rule are not valid for dilute magnesium alloys. Matthiesen's rule states that the resistivity of an alloy may be written as the sum of two terms, one resulting from thermal scattering of carriers and dependent on temperature only, the other resulting from solute atom scattering and independent of temperature. In view of the singular nature of the overlap situation in magnesium, it is not surprising that these terms are not separable. Linde's rule states that the resistivity is linear with concentration. Both of these rules have been found to hold in solid solutions where the electron concentrations are not critical.

In addition to influencing dimensional changes in the solid-solution crystal, the amount of electronic overlap in the simple zone theory also influences the elastic behavior of the magnesium crystal. The elastic constants can be thought of as representing the amount of energy stored in the crystal when it is deformed. If overlap is in progress or is imminent, the Fermi energy of the highest energy electrons can be an important factor in controlling the elastic constants.

## 2.4   Intermetallic Compound Characteristics

The electropositive characteristic of magnesium allows it to form many intermediate phases with other elements. Most of these phases have a narrow solubility range. Indeed, to the student of intermetallic compounds, as such slightly soluble phases are often called, magnesium is one of the most interesting elements. A look at the equilibrium diagrams in Chapter 3 will show how important intermetallic compounds are in the metallurgy of magnesium. It will be noted that investigators have usually felt confident in assigning simple stoichiometry to the many compounds formed in magnesium-based binary systems. The crystal structure of those compounds having a common type or of those of technological importance is generally known. However, the structure of many of these phases is either unknown or in considerable doubt. The assignment of a simple stoichiometry to one of these compounds frequently becomes either (a) plausible or (b) completely unreasonable after the exact crystal structure is known. The three most frequent intermetallic compound structures are discussed in detail below. Less common and usually more complicated structures are described in Chapter 3.

Several magnesium compounds of the type AB crystallize in the CsCl structure. The space lattice is simple cubic, with one atom of each type in the unit cell at the positions 000 and $\frac{1}{2}\frac{1}{2}\frac{1}{2}$. Crystals of this type show some degree of polarity and interesting changes of effective radius are observed as a result. Magnesium acts as the electropositive partner A in the following group of CsCl compounds:

$$\text{MgHg, MgTl, MgAu, and MgAg}$$

It is to be expected that these phases all show varying degrees of "order," but MgAg appears to be the one which disorders to a degree allowing significant study. Magnesium serves as the electronegative component B in the following CsCl type of compounds:

$$\text{SrMg, LaMg, CeMg, and PrMg}$$

The Goldschmidt atomic radius corrected to coordination number 8, 1.57 A, can be thought of as representative of the nonionized magnesium atom in this crystal structure. It has been found that, when magnesium is acting as the electropositive element, the effective radius is smaller, and when it is the electronegative partner, the radius is larger than 1.57 A.

The group IV elements form intermetallic compounds with magnesium in the $CaF_2$ structure:    **1151986**

$$\text{Mg}_2\text{Si, Mg}_2\text{Ge, Mg}_2\text{Sn, and Mg}_2\text{Pb}$$

The space lattice of this structure is face-centered cubic. The unit cell has one group IV atom at the position 000 and two magnesium atoms at the coordinates $\frac{1}{4}\frac{1}{4}\frac{1}{4}$ and $\frac{3}{4}\frac{3}{4}\frac{3}{4}$. This $AB_2$ type of phase of fairly high symmetry is rather loosely packed.

These compounds have been studied in considerable detail because of their interesting electrical properties.[27-30] Winkler has measured the energy gaps, electron and hole mobilities, and intrinsic carrier concentrations for $Mg_2Si$, $Mg_2Ge$, and $Mg_2Sn$, which are intrinsic semiconductors. The energy gaps in electron volts are $(0.77 - 6 \times 10^{-4}T)$, $(0.74 - 8 \times 10^{-4}T)$ and $(0.36 - 3 \times 10^{-4}T)$ respectively, where $T$ is the absolute temperature. Although the Brillouin zone is full in $Mg_2Pb$, it does not behave as a semiconductor but rather as a metallic conductor.

This group contains interesting differences in chemical reaction with water. Apparently, because of a thin oxide layer, the attack of $Mg_2Si$ and $Mg_2Sn$ proceeds only slightly. $Mg_2Ge$ and $Mg_2Pb$, on the other hand, decompose in ordinary room atmosphere in a matter of hours or days into magnesium hydroxide and/or magnesium oxide and germanium or lead.

Interesting studies have been made of the internal friction of molten alloys in the Mg-Pb and Mg-Sn systems.[31, 32] Maxima in the internal friction or viscosity and its "activation energy" approximately at the compositions $Mg_2Pb$ and $Mg_2Sn$ give further evidence of the strong heteropolar bonding in the solid compounds. It is postulated that some of this bonding persists after melting has occurred.

A large and very important group of $AB_2$ intermetallic compounds is especially significant in the science of magnesium because it is called the $MgX_2$ group, after the several magnesium-rich phases that are its prototype. This group is also called the Laves phases because of the large amount of work done on them by Laves and his coworkers. The geometry of packing is such that a radius ratio $R_A/R_B$ of 1.23 is preferred. The type may be subdivided into three groups, the $MgCu_2$, $MgZn_2$, and the $MgNi_2$ types. $MgCu_2$ is face-centered cubic in space lattice with stacking sequence *abcabcabc*. $MgZn_2$ is hexagonal and related to $MgCu_2$ in the same way as simple hexagonal close-packed structures are related to simple face-centered cubic structures, i.e., with stacking *ababab*. $MgNi_2$ is hexagonal with the intermediate stacking sequences of *abacabac*. The $MgX_2$ group has, according to Laves, more representatives than any other metallic structure type, with over 80 having been identified so far. Magnesium once again shows the characteristic duality by participating in this group both as the A and B element. As the former it is contained in the three prototypes already mentioned. As the latter it appears in the following Laves phases:

$$CaMg_2, \; SrMg_2, \; BaMg_2, \; CeMg_2, \; and \; LaMg_2$$

The ternary systems Mg-Cu-Zn, Mg-Ni-Zn, Mg-Cu-Ni, and others based on the magnesium-containing Laves phases have been studied extensively.[33-36] The interesting structural changes that have been observed in transition from one binary to another in ternary systems have been systematized and analyzed to some degree in terms of the electron theories of alloys.

## 2.5 Ordering in Solid Solutions

Superstructure or long-range order has been clearly identified in phases having the simplified stoichiometry $MgCd_3$, $Mg_3Cd$, $MgCd$, $MgAg$, $MgIn$, and $MgIn_2$.

$Mg_3Cd$ and $MgCd_3$ are regarded as the classic ordered phases in the hexagonal close-packed structure. The close-packed or basal plane is the one which most clearly shows the alternate locations of the magnesium and cadmium atoms. The atomic positions were found by x-ray diffraction to be as follows: [37]

$$Mg \text{ in } Mg_3Cd \quad 000; \tfrac{1}{6}\tfrac{1}{3}\tfrac{1}{2} \quad Cd \text{ in } Mg_3Cd \quad \tfrac{1}{2}\tfrac{1}{2}0$$

$$\text{or} \quad \tfrac{1}{2}00; \tfrac{2}{3}\tfrac{1}{3}\tfrac{1}{2} \quad \text{or} \quad \tfrac{1}{6}\tfrac{5}{6}\tfrac{1}{2}$$

$$Cd \text{ in } MgCd_3 \quad 0\tfrac{1}{2}0; \tfrac{2}{3}\tfrac{5}{6}\tfrac{1}{2} \quad Mg \text{ in } MgCd_3$$

The ordering involves the substitution of a B atom in the center position of each rhombic group of A atoms in the close-packed planes. The atomic coordinates above are referred to the lattice parameters of the ordered cell, $a'$ and $c$ rather than those of the disordered cell, $a$ and $c$. The following values were measured for $Mg_3Cd$ at room temperature:

$$a' = 6.26 \text{ A} \quad a = 3.13 \text{ A} \quad c = 5.07 \text{ A} \quad \text{density} = 3.49$$

The following values were measured for $MgCd_3$:

$$a' = 5.86 \text{ A} \quad a = 2.93 \text{ A} \quad c = 5.53 \text{ A}$$

Dehlinger concluded from his results that the $Mg_3Cd$ phase had a constant $c/a$ ratio $= 1.62$ over its composition range of existence, that the $MgCd_3$ phase had a $c/a = 1.89$, and that they enjoyed a two-phase equilibrium over the range 25–65 atomic % Mg. Kornilov has concluded from dilatometric data that the ordering of both $Mg_3Cd$ and $MgCd_3$ follow the kinetics of a monomolecular chemical reaction.[38] The correctness of these conclusions as well as the mechanism of the ordering need further study. The existence of equilibrium between two ordered phases is hard to reconcile with many present-day concepts of the process of long-range ordering.

The structural determinations of Dehlinger were confirmed by Riederer for the $Mg_3Cd$ and $MgCd_3$ superstructures.[39] In addition he concluded from x-ray powder-pattern studies that the ordered structure MgCd is rhombic with cell parameters:

$$a = 10.65 \text{ A} \qquad b = 6.38 \text{ A} \qquad c = 5.05 \text{ A}$$

The stoichiometry MgAg is displayed by an ordered phase of the CsCl structure type discussed in Section 2.4. Here the magnesium atoms appear at the corners and the silver atoms at the centers of the body-centered cubic unit cell.[40]

The quasi-binary system $Mg$-$AgCd_3$ shows ordering of the same type as $Mg_3Cd$ in the range 37–70 atomic % Mg and of the same type as MgCd in the near vicinity of 50 atomic % Mg.[41]

The MgIn phase has been reported to show long-range order of the AuCu type. This type presents a face-centered cubic space lattice with segregation of the two atomic species on alternate {001} planes.

Short-range order, the preference for unlike neighbors, has been studied in considerable detail for the body-centered cubic Mg-Li alloys by Herbstein and Averbach.[42] Careful x-ray diffuse-scattering measurements were made to obtain the first short-range order coefficient $\alpha_1$ as a function of atom fraction of lithium, $m_{Li}$, Fig. 2.14. This coefficient is defined by the equation:

$$\alpha_i = 1 - \frac{P_i^A}{m_A}$$

where $P_i^A$ is the probability that an A atom is in the $i$th shell about a B atom and $m_A$ is the atom fraction of A atoms.

The small-angle scattering of x-rays from solid solutions also reveals information about the relative size of the atoms A and B. It has been found several times since this effect has been discovered that the atomic sizes changed with composition of a binary alloy in such a way as to change the deviation of the atomic centers from the average positions of the lattice. However, in general the A-B distances could be predicted at any alloying level from the effective A-A and B-B distances. In the Mg-Li body-centered cubic solutions, the Mg-Li distances are considerably shorter than the values one would expect from the lattice parameters and the independent size change of the

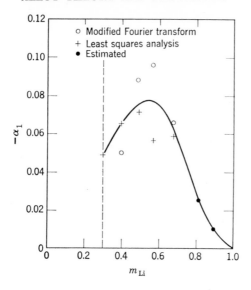

Fig. 2.14. Short-range order coefficient, $\alpha_1$, in the Mg-Li system, as a function of composition.[42]

individual atoms. This evidence of a special interaction of the Mg and Li atoms harmonizes with the existence of short-range order and also with the minimum in the lattice parameter-versus-composition curve for the body-centered cubic solid solution. As in the reference to Levinson,[24] cited in Section 2.3, Herbstein [43] also found a minimum in this relationship, although at 65 rather than at 50 atomic % Li.

## References

1. W. Hume-Rothery and G. V. Raynor, *The Structure of Metals and Alloys*, Institute of Metals, London, 1956.
2. L. A. Carapella, "Fundamental Alloying Nature of Magnesium," *Metal Progr.*, **48**, 297 (1945).
3. H. Jones, "Application of the Bloch Theory to the Study of Alloys and of the Properties of Bismuth," *Proc. Phys. Soc. (London)*, **A147**, 400 (1934).
4. H. Jones, "Structural and Elastic Properties of Metals," *Physica*, **15**, 13 (1949).
5. H. Jones, "The Effect of Electron Concentration on the Lattice Spacings in Magnesium Solid Solutions," *Phil. Mag.*, **41**, 663 (1950).
6. W. Hume-Rothery, *Atomic Theory for Students of Metallurgy*, Institute of Metals, London, 1955.

7. C. Kittel, *Introduction to Solid State Physics*, 2nd edition, John Wiley & Sons, New York, 1956.

8. N. F. Mott and H. Jones, *The Theory of the Properties of Metals and Alloys*, Clarendon Press, Oxford, 1936.

9. F. Seitz, *The Modern Theory of Solids*, McGraw-Hill Book Co., New York, 1940.

10. A. H. Wilson, *The Theory of Metals*, Cambridge University Press, Cambridge, England, 1954.

11. A discussion of the various approximations is given by J. C. Slater, *Handbuch der Physik*, Vol. 19, Springer, Berlin, 1956, pp. 10–47.

12. M. Trlifaj, "Electron Theory of Metallic Magnesium," *Czechoslov. J. Phys.*, **1**, 110 (1952).

13. J. B. Goodenough, "A Theory of the Deviation from Close Packing in Hexagonal Metal Crystals," *Phys. Rev.*, **89**, 282 (1953).

14. J. W. McClure, "Axial Ratios in Hexagonal Crystals," *Phys. Rev.*, **98**, 449 (1955).

15. P. M. Marcus, "Anisotropic Electronic Stress and Mg Alloys," *Phys. Rev.*, **98**, 1552 (1955).

16. H. W. B. Skinner, "Soft X-ray Spectroscopy of Solids. Part I. K- and L-Emission Spectra from Elements of the First Two Groups," *Phil. Trans. Roy. Soc. London*, **A239**, 95 (1940).

17. W. M. Cady and D. H. Tomboulian, "The L-Emission Bands of Sodium, Magnesium and Aluminum," *Phys. Rev.*, **S9**, 381 (1941).

18. R. S. Busk, "Lattice Parameters of Magnesium Alloys," *Trans. AIME*, **188**, 1460 (1950).

19. G. V. Raynor, "The Lattice Spacings of the Primary Solid Solutions of Ag. Cd and In in Mg," *Proc. Roy. Soc. (London)*, **A174**, 457 (1940).

20. W. Hume-Rothery and G. V. Raynor, "The Apparent Sizes of Atoms in Metallic Crystals with Special Reference to Aluminum and Indium and the Electron State of Magnesium," *Proc. Roy. Soc. (London)*, **A177**, 27 (1940).

21. G. V. Raynor, "The Lattice Spacings of the Primary Solid Solutions in Magnesium of the Metals of Group IIIB and of Tin and Lead," *Proc. Roy. Soc. (London)*, **A180,** 107 (1942).

22. R. S. Busk, "Effect of Temperature on the Lattice Parameters of Magnesium Alloys," *Trans. AIME*, **194**, 207 (1952).

23. W. Hume-Rothery and G. V. Raynor, "The Equilibrium and Lattice Spacing Relations in the System Mg-Cd," *Proc. Roy. Soc. (London)*, **A174**, 471 (1940).

24. D. W. Levinson, "On the Lattice Parameter of Mg-Li $\beta$ Alloys," *Acta Met.*, **3**, 294 (1955).

25. A. I. Schindler and E. I. Salkovitz, "Brillouin Zone Investigation of Mg Alloys. I. Hall Effect and Conductivity," *Phys. Rev.*, **91**, 1320 (1953).

26. E. I. Salkovitz, A. I. Schindler, and E. W. Kammer, "Transport Properties in Dilute Binary Magnesium Alloys," *Phys. Rev.*, **105**, 887 (1957).

27. W. D. Robertson and H. H. Uhlig, "Electrical Properties of Intermetallic Compounds $Mg_2Sn$ and $Mg_2Pb$," *Trans. AIME*, **180**, 345 (1949).

28. R. F. Blunt, H. P. R. Frederikse, and W. R. Hosler, "Electrical and Optical Properties of Intermetallic Compounds. IV—Magnesium Stannide," *Phys. Rev.*, **100**, 663 (1955).

29. U. Winkler, "Electrical Properties of the Intermetallic Compounds, $Mg_2Si$, $Mg_2Ge$, $Mg_2Sn$, and $Mg_2Pb$," *Helv. Phys. Acta*, **23**, 633–666 (1955).

30. H. P. R. Frederikse, W. R. Hosler, and D. E. Roberts, "Electrical Conduction in Magnesium Stannide at Low Temperatures," *Phys. Rev.*, **103**, 67 (1956).

31. E. Gebhardt, M. Becker, and E. Tragner, "Über die Eigenschaften metallischer Schmelzen. X—Die innere Reibung flüssiger Mg-Pb Legierungen," *Z. Metallk.*, **46**, 90 (1955).

32. E. Gebhardt, M. Becker, and H. Sebastian, "Über die Eigenschaften metallischer Schmelzen. XI—Die innere Reibung flüssiger Magnesium-Zinn-Legierungen," *Z. Metallk.*, **46**, 669 (1955).

33. K. H. Lieser and H. Witte, "Untersuchungen in den ternaren Systemen Mg-Cu-Zn, Mg-Ni-Zn und Mg-Cu-Ni," *Z. Metallk.*, **43**, 396 (1952).

34. R. L. Berry and G. V. Raynor, "The Crystal Chemistry of the Laves Phases," *Acta Cryst.*, **6**, 178 (1953).

35. H. Klee and H. Witte, "Magnetische Suszeptibilitäten ternarer Magnesium Legierungen und ihre Deutung vom Standpunkt der Elektronentheorie der Metalle," *Z. Phys. Chem. (Leipzig)*, **202**, 352 (1954).

36. V. I. Mikheeva and G. C. Bakaian, "Chemical Nature of Tertiary Intermetallic Phases in Mg-Cu-Zn and Mg-Cu-Ni Systems," *Dan SSSR*, **109**, 785–786 (1956).

37. U. Dehlinger, "Röntgenographische Untersuchungen am System Cd-Mg," *Z. anorg. u. allgem. Chem.*, **194**, 223 (1930).

38. I. I. Kornilov, "Kinetics of the Formation of $Mg_3Cd$ and $MgCd_3$ from Solid Solutions of Mg-Cd Alloys," *Compt. rend. acad. sci. U.R.S.S.*, **19**, 157 (1938).

39. K. Riederer, "Das System Magnesium-Kadmium," *Z. Metallk.*, **29**, 423 (1937).

40. H. R. Letner and S. S. Sidhu, "An X-ray Diffraction Study of the Silver-Magnesium Alloy System," *J. Appl. Phys.*, **18**, 833 (1947).

41. F. Laves and K. Moeller, "Über die Mischkristallreihe $Mg-AgCd_3$ im ternaren System Magnesium-Silber-Kadmium," *Z. Metallk.*, **29**, 185 (1937).

42. F. H. Herbstein and B. L. Averbach, "Structure of Lithium-Magnesium Solid Solutions II," *Acta Met.*, **4**, 415 (1956).

43. F. H. Herbstein and B. L. Averbach, "Structure of Lithium-Magnesium Solid Solutions I," *Acta Met.*, **4**, 407 (1956).

# 3

# Magnesium
# Alloy
# Systems

The binary and ternary systems which are reasonably well understood are presented in the following pages. The diagrams are the result of a comparative examination of three recent compendia * supplemented by certain original publications. Complete references to original literature which are extensive may be found in these compendia. Some judgments and comments are made with respect to obscure systems. In other cases, it suffices here to point out controversies, incompletely or partially resolved, concerning the systems of great contemporary interest. It is readily admitted that, in order to gain the best understanding of any particular diagram, the reader should review the literature which contributed to it.

The magnesium-rich solid solution is called $\alpha$, and successively more solute-rich phases are termed $\beta$, $\gamma$, $\delta$, $\epsilon$, etc. Only single-phase fields are labeled in order to increase diagram readability.

A semitabular form of showing information supplementary to the diagrams is given for the first system, i.e., of Mg-Ag. From then on the individual sections of the accessory information are presented only by number, i.e., without repetition of the titles. Asterisks refer to references in each section.

* *Metals Handbook*, American Society for Metals, Cleveland, Ohio, 1948 Edition, hereafter referred to as MH.

W. Rostoker and D. W. Levinson, "The Constitution of Binary Magnesium Alloys," Armour Research Foundation of Illinois Institute of Technology, Summary Report, Part I, Contract No. DA-11-022-ORD-1645, sponsored by Frankford Arsenal, Philadelphia, hereafter referred to as RL.

M. Hansen, *Constitution of Binary Alloys*, written in cooperation with K. Anderko, McGraw-Hill Book Co., New York, 1958, hereafter referred to as Hansen.

## 3.1  Mg-Ag

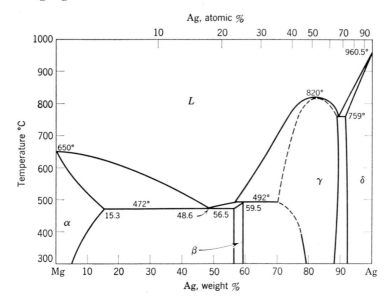

1. Alloying element; group in periodic table; structure; interatomic distance $d$ (A) in elemental crystal; size factor $S$, with respect to magnesium in percent:

Silver, group Ib, F.C.C., $d = 2.89$, $S = -10$.

2. Solubility of alloying element in magnesium:

| 200°C | 300 | 400 | 472 |
|-------|-----|-----|-----|
| 1.6%  | 3.9 | 9.0 | 15.3 |

3. Intermediate phases:

| Symbol | Approximate Stoichiometry | Structure (Strukturbericht Notation) |
|--------|---------------------------|--------------------------------------|
| $\beta$ | $Mg_3Ag$ | Complicated, not solved at present |
| $\gamma$ | $MgAg$ | Cubic B2 (CsCl type), Ordering maximum at 50 atomic % where $a = 3.305$ A |

4. Doubtful or controversial regions: Width of $\gamma$-field.

5. Present commercial significance: Minor, resulting from use in forging alloys to take advantage of extended solubility range.

6. References:
   (a) Diagram from MH, slightly modified according to Hansen.
   (b) Latest work by H. R. Letner and S. S. Sidhu, *J. Appl. Phys.*,
       **18,** 833 (1947).

## 3.2  Mg-Al

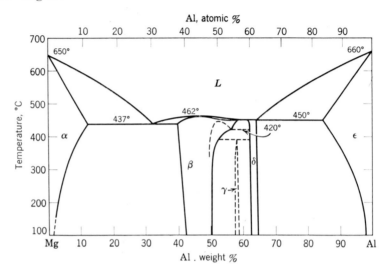

1. Aluminum, group III, F.C.C., $d = 2.86, S = -10$.

2.

| | 200°C | 250 | 300 | 350 | 400 | 437 |
|---|---|---|---|---|---|---|
| | 3.2% | 4.1 | 5.3 | 7.3 | 10.6 | 12.7 |

3. $\beta$   $Mg_{17}Al_{12}$    Cubic A12 ($\alpha$-Mn type)
                            58 atoms/unit cell
                            $a = 10.52$ A

   $\gamma$   MgAl        $d$ values have been measured on a 42 weight %
                            Mg alloy *

   $\delta$   $Mg_2Al_3$   Cubic Fd3m is more probable
                            1172 atoms/unit cell
                            $a = 28.13$ A
                            Hexagonal has been reported
                            $a = 11.38$ A, $c = 17.87$ A

4. Widths of $\beta$-, $\gamma$-, and $\delta$-fields are uncertain. The presence of a
eutectoid decomposition of $\gamma$ into $\beta + \delta$ at some temperature below
335°C has been reported.*

5. Extreme. Aluminum is a constituent of almost all contemporary casting and wrought alloys designed for normal temperature application. Magnesium-rich solid solution age-hardens by both continuous and cellular precipitation.

6. (a) Diagram from G. V. Raynor, *Annotated Equilibrium Diagrams No. 5*, The Institute of Metals, London, 1945.

* (b) Recent commentary on the controversial central portion by J. B. Clark and F. N. Rhines, *Trans. AIME*, **209**, 6 (1957).

## 3.3 Mg-Au

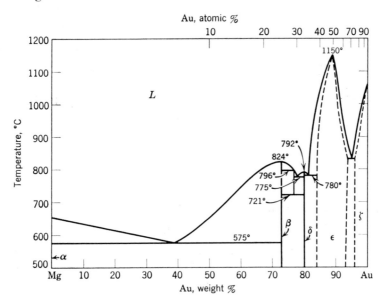

1. Gold, group Ib, F.C.C., $d = 2.88$, $S = -10$.

2. Slight; decreases $a$ and decreases $c/a$.

3. $\beta$    $Mg_3Au$    Hexagonal $Do_{18}$ ($Na_3As$ type)
                        8 atoms/unit cell
                        $a = 4.64$ A, $c = 8.46$ A

   $\gamma$    $Mg_5Au_2$    Apparently not known

   $\delta$    $Mg_2Au$    Apparently not known

   $\epsilon$    MgAu    Cubic B2 (CsCl type)
                        $a = 3.266$ A

4. Gold-rich side of diagram needs more study.

5. None.

6. Diagram from Hansen.

## 3.4   Mg-Ba

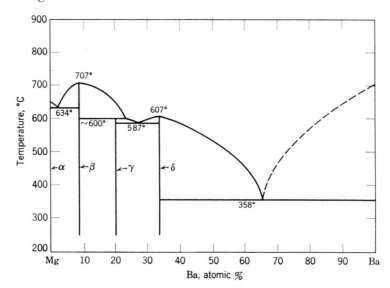

1. Barium, group IIa, B.C.C., $d = 4.35$, $S = 36$.

2. Slight; increases $a$ and increases $c/a$.

3. $\beta$    $Mg_{10.5}Ba$    Hexagonal $D2_d$ ($CaCu_5$ type)
   $a = 10.58$ A, $c = 10.53$ A

   $\gamma$    $Mg_4Ba$    Apparently not known

   $\delta$    $Mg_2Ba$    Hexagonal C14 ($MgZn_2$ type)
   12 atoms/unit cell
   $a = 6.649$ A, $c = 10.676$ A

4. Little is known of high-barium alloy equilibria.

5. None.

6. (a) Diagram from W. Klemm and F. Dinckelacker, *Z. anorg. Chem.*, **255**, 2 (1947), with modification of β-composition.

   (b) β-structure and composition determined by E. Goldish and R. E. Marsh (unpublished).

## 3.5 Mg-Bi

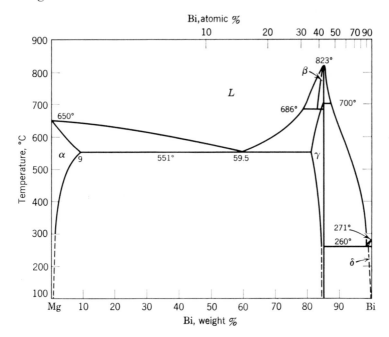

1. Bismuth, rhombohedral, group V, $d = 3.11$, $S = -3$.

2.

| 250°C | 300 | 350 | 400 | 450 | 500 | 525 | 553 |
|---|---|---|---|---|---|---|---|
| 0.1% | 0.33 | 0.79 | 1.53 | 2.81 | 4.95 | 6.56 | 9.05 |

3. $\beta$    $Mg_3Bi_2$     Apparently not known

   $\gamma$    $Mg_3Bi_2$     Hexagonal D5$_2$ ($La_2O_3$ type)

                     5 atoms/unit cell

                     $a = 4.675$ A, $c = 7.416$ A

4. Low-temperature solid solubility uncertain. $(\beta + \gamma)$-equilibrium uncertain.

5. None.

6. Diagram from MH.

## 3.6   Mg-Ca

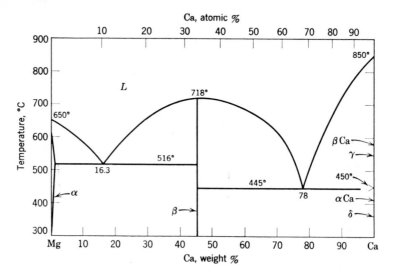

1. Calcium, F.C.C., group IIa, $d = 3.93$, $S = 23$.

2.                   *350°C      400      450      500      516
              0.1%        0.2      0.5      0.8      0.9

3. $\beta$     $Mg_2Ca$     Hexagonal C14 ($MgZn_2$ type)
              Laves phase
              12 atoms/unit cell
              $a = 6.23$ A, $c = 10.12$ A

4. Solid solubility of magnesium in calcium unknown.   Burke finds solubility of calcium in magnesium considerably less than the previously accepted values.

5. Calcium is sometimes added to rolling and extrusion alloys containing aluminum and zinc.   It influences the rollability and the preferred orientation considerably.   It also is an essential ingredient in commercial Mg-Mn alloys.   It is used in some Mg-Al-Zn casting alloys to control oxidation and influence heat treatment.

6. (a)  Diagram from MH, with modifications according to the data of
   *(b) E. C. Burke, *Trans. AIME*, **203**, 285 (1955).

## 3.7 Mg-Cd

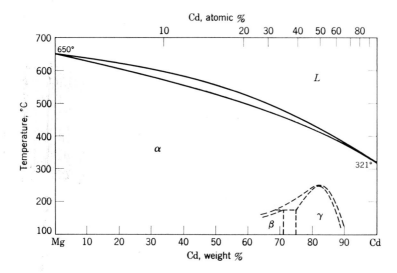

1. Cadmium, group IIb, H.C.P., $d = 2.98$, $S = -7$.

2. Complete solubility.

3. Ordered structures $Mg_3Cd$, $MgCd$, and $MgCd_3$ discussed in Section 5.5.

4. Existence of equilibrium between ordered phases highly controversial. This is in part a reflection of the general controversy on the topic of order-disorder equilibrium.

5. None, although of considerable theoretical interest.

6. Diagram from MH.

## 3.8   Mg-Ce

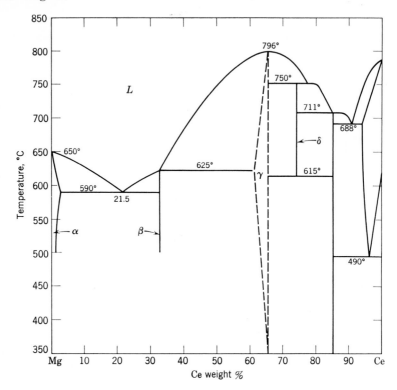

1. Cerium, rare earth element, F.C.C., $d = 3.65$, $S = 14$.

2. 
| 337°C | 500 | 550 | 590 | increases $a$ and decreases $c/a$ |
|---|---|---|---|---|
| 0.15% | 0.5 | 1.0 | 1.6 | |

3. 
| $\beta$ | $Mg_{12}Ce$ | (formerly $Mg_9Ce$) * | Hexagonal D2$_a$ (TiBe$_{12}$ type) $a \cong c \cong 10.3$ A Possesses a complicated kind of disorder |
|---|---|---|---|
| $\gamma$ | $Mg_3Ce$ | | Cubic Do$_3$ (BiF$_3$ type) $a = 7.46$ A |
| $\delta$ | $Mg_2Ce$ | | Cubic C15 (MgCu$_2$ type) Laves phase 24 atoms/unit cell $a = 8.70$ A |

ε    MgCe                        Cubic B2 (CsCl type)
                                 $a = 3.90$ A

4. Composition of the β-phase deserves more study.

5. Much commercial significance as principal alloying element for high-temperature creep-resistant magnesium alloys.

6. (a) Diagram from MH, also from R. Vogel and T. Heumann, *Z. Metallk.*, **38**, 1 (1947) with modifications of composition of
  *(b) β-phase determined by A. Miller (unpublished).

## 3.9  Mg-Cu

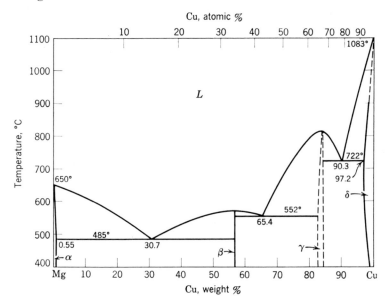

1. Copper, group Ib, F.C.C., $d = 2.56$, $S = -20$.

2.                    300° C      400      480
                      0.20%       0.30     0.55

3. β    Mg₂Cu    Face-centered orthorhombic $C_b$
                  48 atoms/unit cell
                  $a = 5.284$ A, $b = 9.07$ A, $c = 18.25$ A

   γ    MgCu₂    F.C.C. C15
                  24 atoms/unit cell
                  $a = 7.03$–$7.05$ A

4. Solubility range of γ needs more study.

5. None.

6. Diagram from MH.

## 3.10  Mg-Fe

1. Iron, transition element, B.C.C., $d = 2.48$, $S = -22$.

2. 0.026% iron soluble in magnesium just above its melting point according to W. Bulian and E. Fahrenhorst, Z. *Metallk.*, **33,** 31 (1941).

3. None, the equilibrium phase is $\alpha$-iron.

4. The solid solubility is 0.001 weight % Fe and the eutectic occurs at 0.006% Fe according to A. S. Yue, The Dow Chemical Company.

5. None. Iron is a most harmful second-phase impurity in magnesium, fostering corrosion when present in certain amounts and particle size distributions.

## 3.11  Mg-Ga

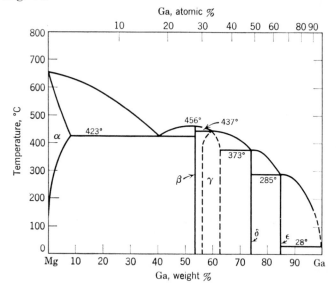

1. Gallium, group III, orthorhombic, $d = 2.44$, $S = -24$.

2. As shown in diagram.

3. $\beta$     $Mg_5Ga_2$     Orthorhombic $D8_g$
                          28 atoms/unit cell
                          $a = 13.72$ A, $b = 7.02$ A, $c = 6.02$ A

γ   Mg₂Ga   Close to hexagonal C22 (Fe₂P type)
             18 atoms/unit cell
             $a = 7.861$ A, $c = 6.958$ A
δ   MgGa    Apparently not known
ε   MgGa₂   Apparently not known

4. γ-Solubility range uncertain.

5. None.

6. Diagram from H. Grober and V. Hauk, *Z. Metallk.*, **41**, 191 (1950) with amplification by RL.


### 3.12 Mg-Ge

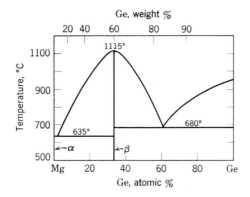

1. Germanium, group IV, diamond cubic, $d = 2.45$, $S = -24$.

2. Slight.

3. β   Mg₂Ge   F.C.C. C1 (CaF₂ type)
                12 atoms/unit cell
                $a = 6.390$ A

4. None.

5. None.

6. Diagram from Hansen.

## 3.13 Mg-Hg

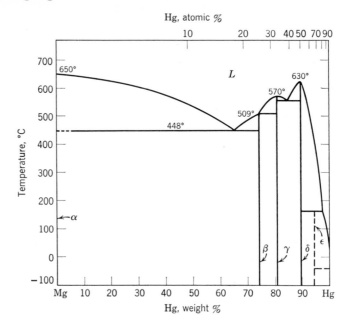

1. Mercury, group IIb, rhombohedral, $d = 3.01$, $S = -6$.

2. Uncertain.

3. $\beta$     $Mg_3Hg$       Hexagonal $Do_{18}$ ($Na_3As$ type)
                                 8 atoms/unit cell
                                   $a = 4.868$ A, $c = 8.656$ A

    $\gamma$     $Mg_5Hg_3$      Hexagonal D8 ($Mn_5Si_3$ type)
                                   16 atoms/unit cell
                                   $a = 8.260$ A, $c = 5.931$ A

    $\delta$     $MgHg$        Cubic B2 (CsCl type)
                                   $a = 3.449$ A

    $\epsilon$     $MgHg_2$       Tetragonal C11 ($CaC_2$ type)
                                   6 atoms/unit cell
                                   $a = 3.838$ A, $c = 8.799$ A

4. Solubility in $\alpha$ needs determination.

5. None.

6. Diagram from Hansen.

### 3.14  Mg-K

1. Potassium, group Ia, B.C.C., $d = 4.63$, $S = 45$.

2. The two elements are mutually insoluble in the solid.  Magnesium is insoluble in liquid potassium.

3. None.

4. Solubility in liquid above 650°C is unknown.

5. None.

### 3.15  Mg-La

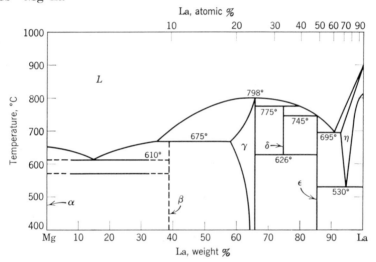

La, atomic %

1. Lanthanum, transition element, H.C.P., $d = 3.74$, $S = 17$.

2. Approximately 0.4% La at 577°C.

3. $\beta$     Mg$_9$La     Unknown but, if this phase is isomorphous with the corresponding phase in the Mg-Ce system, its composition should be close to Mg$_{12}$La

    $\gamma$     Mg$_3$La     Cubic Do$_3$ (BiF$_3$ type)
                              16 atoms/unit cell
                              $a = 7.493$ A

    $\delta$     Mg$_2$La     Cubic C15 (MgCu$_2$ type)
                              Laves phase
                              24 atoms/unit cell
                              $a = 8.79$ A

$\epsilon$     MgLa      Cubic B2 (CsCl type)

$a = 3.97$ A

4. Equilibria of entire system deserve redetermination.

5. Lanthanum is a significant component of "misch metal" which is added to magnesium for creep resistance and tensile strength in both casting and wrought alloys at high temperature.

6. Diagram from R. Vogel and T. Heumann, *Z. Metallk.*, **38,** 1 (1947) with modifications according to RL.

### 3.16 Mg-Li

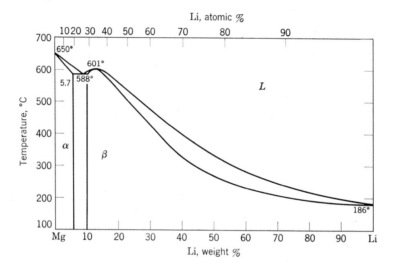

1. Lithium, group Ia, B.C.C., $d = 3.04, S = -5$.

2. Nearly constant at 5.7%. Some investigators found increasing solubility, others decreasing solubility with increasing temperature.

3. None.

4. Some investigators have reported evidence of superstructure in the $\beta$-field. Later workers, in the course of studying short-range order in the body-centered cubic phase, were unable to find any evidence of long-range order.

5. Considerable potential commercial significance. The body-centered cubic alloys have excited interest because of lightness and work-

ability. Control of corrosion and precipitation is still incomplete in Mg-Li-based alloys.

6. Diagram from MH.

### 3.17 Mg-Mn

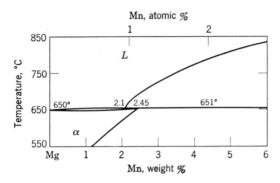

1. Manganese, transition element, complex cubic, $d = 2.24, S = -30$.

2.

| | 455°C | 540 | 620 | 651 |
|---|---|---|---|---|
| | 0.25% | 1.00 | 2.06 | 2.45 |

3. None. The equilibrium phase $\beta$ is $\alpha$-manganese.

4. High-manganese end undetermined. Solid solubility in $\alpha$ is somewhat controversial. Hansen shows higher values than MH.

5. Manganese is of great commercial importance in increasing corrosion resistance and strength of cast and wrought alloys. It is normally present as a significant residual even when not intentionally added.

6. Diagram from MH.

## 3.18   Mg-Na

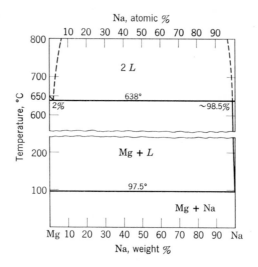

1. Sodium, group Ia, B.C.C., $d = 3.72, S = 16$.

2. The two elements are mutually insoluble in the solid.

3. None.

4. Solubility in the liquid above 638°C is unknown.

5. None.

6. Diagram from C. H. Mathewson, *Z. anorg. Chem.*, **48,** 193 (1906).

## 3.19 Mg-Ni

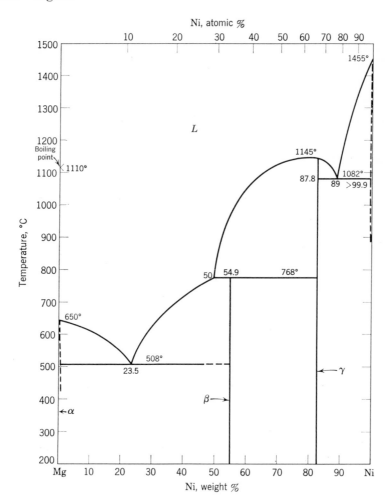

1. Nickel, transition element, F.C.C., $d = 2.49$, $S = -22$.

2. Very small.

3. $\beta$     $Mg_2Ni$     Hexagonal $C_a$
   18 atoms/unit cell
   $a = 5.19$ A, $c = 13.22$ A

$\gamma$   MgNi$_2$    Hexagonal C36
Laves phase
24 atoms/unit cell
$a = 4.81$ A, $c = 15.80$ A

4. Controversy exists concerning the possible existence of a two-liquid field between 72 and 84% Ni.

5. Nickel is an undesirable impurity because of its promotion of pitting corrosion in magnesium.

6. Diagram from MH.

### 3.20   Mg-Pb

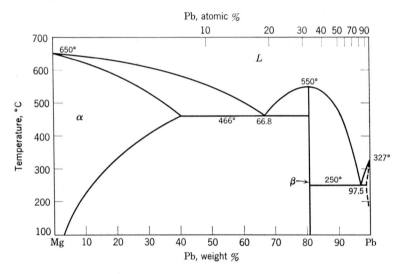

1. Lead, group IV, F.C.C., $d = 3.50$, $S = 9$.

2. Extensive.

3. $\beta$    Mg$_2$Pb    Cubic C1 (CaF$_2$ type)
12 atoms/unit cell
$a = 6.81$–$6.86$ A

4. Higher solubility of lead in magnesium than shown here has been reported.

5. None.

6. Diagram from MH.

## 3.21 Mg-Sb

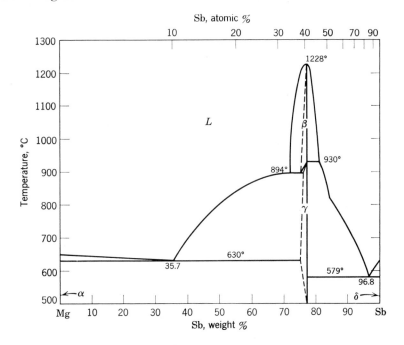

1. Antimony, group V, rhombohedral, $d = 2.90$, $S = -9$.

2. Very slight.

3. $\beta$    $Mg_3Sb_2$    May be cubic $D5_3$ ($Mn_2O_3$ type)

    $\gamma$    $Mg_3Sb_2$    Hexagonal $D5_2$ ($La_2O_3$ type)
                             5 atoms/unit cell
                             $a = 4.582$ A, $c = 7.244$ A

4. Solubility range of $\beta$ and $\gamma$ doubtful.

5. None.

6. Diagram from Hansen.

## 3.22   Mg-Si

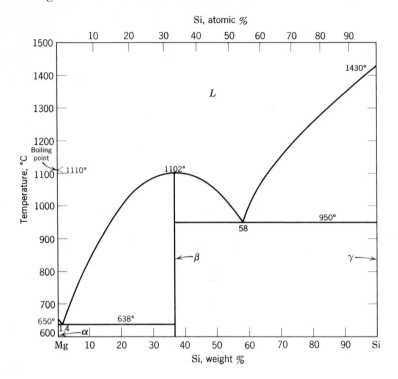

1. Silicon, group IV, diamond cubic, $d = 2.35$, $S = 26$.

2. Very slight.

3. $\beta$      $Mg_2Si$      Cubic C1 ($CaF_2$ type)
   12 atoms/unit cell
   $a = 6.40$ A

4. None.

5. Little commercial significance now; early casting alloys used silicon as a strengthener.

6. Diagram from MH.

## 3.23  Mg-Sn

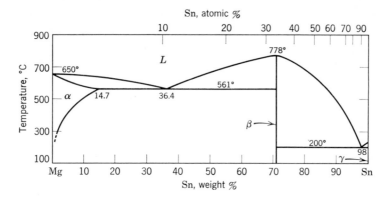

1. Tin, group IV, body-centered tetragonal, $d = 3.02$, $S = -5$.

2.

| 250°C | 300 | 325 | 422 | 475 | 500 | 525 | 560 |
|---|---|---|---|---|---|---|---|
| 0.98% | 1.40 | 1.90 | 5.25 | 8.10 | 9.95 | 11.75 | 14.7 |

3. $\beta$    $Mg_2Sn$    Cubic C1 ($CaF_2$ type)
                    12 atoms/unit cell
                    $a = 6.76$ A

4. None.

5. Little present commercial significance; tin was a constituent of some early hammer-forging alloys.

6. Diagram from MH.

## 3.24  Mg-Th

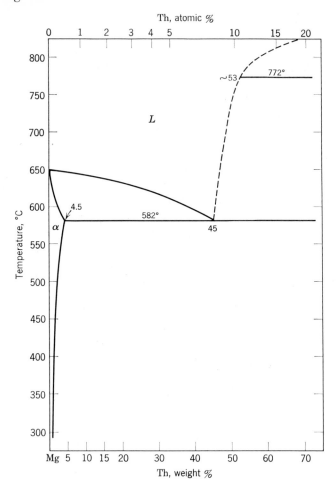

1. Thorium, actinium series element, F.C.C., $d = 3.60$, $S = 12$.

2.
| | 300°C | 400 | 500 | 550 | 582 |
|---|---|---|---|---|---|
| | 0.8% | 1.2 | 2.3 | 3.1 | 4.5 |

3. $\beta$     Mg$_5$Th     Cubic
         or          $a = 14.3$–$14.4$ A
     Mg$_4$Th

4. Uncertainty concerning composition of $\beta$.   Thorium-rich end of system undetermined.

5. Great commercial importance as a principal alloying element for high-temperature creep-resistant magnesium alloys.

6. Diagram from A. S. Yamamoto and W. Rostoker, *Trans. ASM*, **50,** 1090 (1958).

### 3.25 Mg-Tl

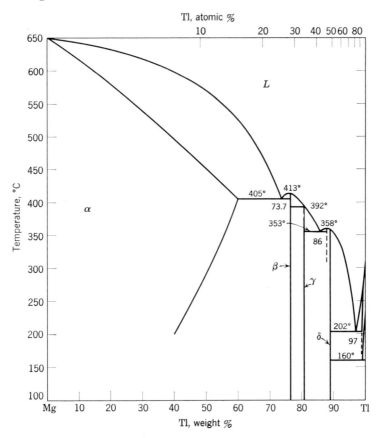

1. Thallium, group IIIb, H.C.P., $d = 3.40$, $S = 7$.

2. Extensive.

3. $\beta$     $Mg_5Tl_2$     Orthorhombic D8 ($Mg_5Ga_2$ type)
                                        28 atoms/unit cell

    $\gamma$     $Mg_2Tl$     Hexagonal approx. C22 ($Fe_2P$ type)
                                          $a = 8.12$ A, $c = 7.35$ A

δ    MgTl        Cubic B2 (CsCl type)
                 $a = 3.64$ A

4. Solid solubility uncertain in both terminal solid solutions.

5. None.

6. Diagram from Hansen.

## 3.26  Mg-Zn

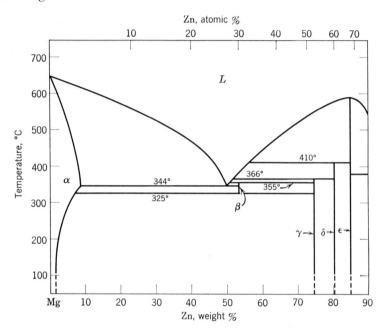

1. Zinc, group IIb, H.C.P., $d = 2.66$, $S = -17$.

2.              150°C     200     250     300     340
                1.7%      2.0     3.3     6.0     8.4

3. β    $Mg_7Zn_3$     $d$ values have been measured *
   γ    MgZn           Structure is uncertain
   δ    $Mg_2Zn_3$     $d$ values have been measured *
   ε    $MgZn_2$       Hexagonal C14
                       Laves phase
                       12 atoms/unit cell
                       $a = 5.16$ A, $c = 8.50$ A

$\nu$    $Mg_2Zn_{11}$    Cubic D8 ($Mg_2Cu_6Al_5$ type)
                        39 atoms/unit cell
                        $a = 8.55$ A

4. Some controversy exists concerning the eutectoid decomposition of the $Mg_7Zn_3$ phase.**

5. Very important; zinc has great strengthening properties in both cast and wrought alloys.

6.   *(a)  Diagram from J. B. Clark and F. N. Rhines, *Trans. AIME*, **209,** 425 (1957).

   **(b)  K. P. Anderko et al., *Trans. ASM*, **49, 778** (1957).

## 3.27   Mg-Zr

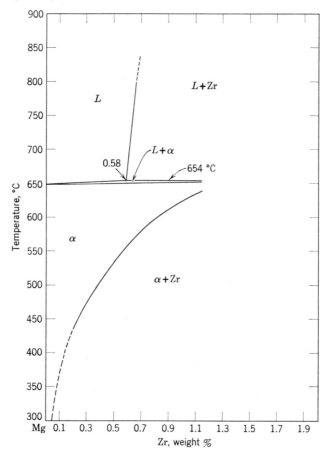

Zr, weight %

1. Zirconium, transition element, H.C.P., $d = 3.16$, $S = -1$.

2.        300°C        400        500        650
        $<0.1\%$        0.1–0.2        0.4        $>1.1$

3. $\beta$-phase structure probably is $\alpha$-Zr.

4. High-zirconium alloys need more study.

5. Zirconium is an important grain refiner in magnesium alloys.

6. Diagram from J. H. Schaum and H. C. Burnett, *J. Res. Natl. Bur. Standards*, **49**, 155 (1952).

### 3.28   Mg-Al-Ca

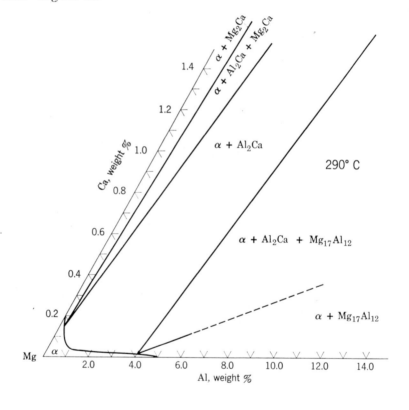

## Mg-Al-Ca (Cont.)

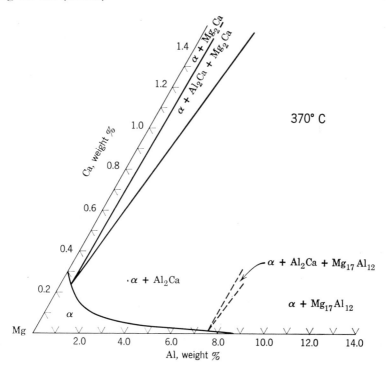

## Mg-Al-Ca (Cont.)

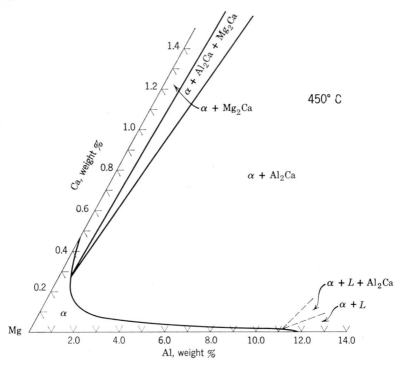

Isothermal sections of the magnesium-rich corner of this system at 290°, 370°, and 450°C are taken from the work of J. A. Catterall and R. J. Pleasance, *J. Inst. Met.*, **86,** 189 (1957). The important phase $Al_2Ca$ is cubic C15 ($MgCu_2$ type) with $a = 8.04$ A and 24 atoms/unit cell. The system is important commercially because of the frequent addition of calcium to Mg-Al-based wrought and casting alloys.

## 3.29 Mg-Al-Zn

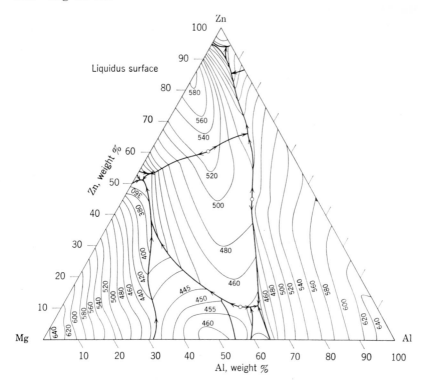

## Mg-Al-Zn (Cont.)

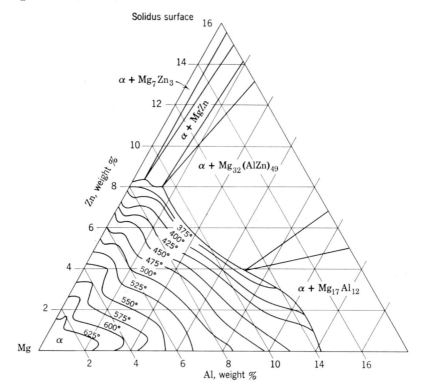

Solidus surface

## Mg-Al-Zn (Cont.)

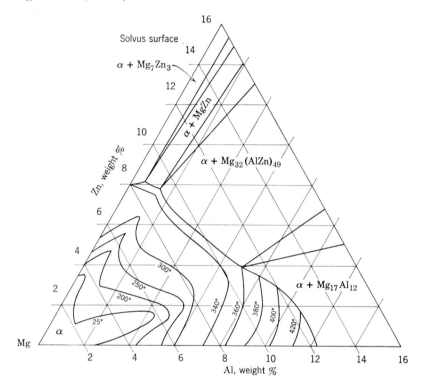

The liquidus, solidus, and solvus surfaces are from V. I. Mikheeva, *Magnesium Alloys with Aluminum and Zinc*, Publishing House of the Academy of Science of the U.S.S.R., Moscow, 1946. The ternary intermetallic phase $\lambda$ has a long range of zinc solubility (20–70%). It is cubic $D8_e$ ($Mg_{32}X_{49}$ type) in structure with $a = 14.16$ A and 162 atoms/unit cell according to Bergman, Waugh, and Pauling, *Acta Cryst.*, **10**, 254 (1957). Another ternary phase of approximate composition 40% Mg, 40% Zn, and 20% Al has been discovered by J. B. Clark. Although the structure is not yet determined, $d$ values have been measured for this phase.

This ternary system is of primary importance in the technology of casting and wrought alloys for normal-temperature application.

## 3.30   Mg-Li-Al

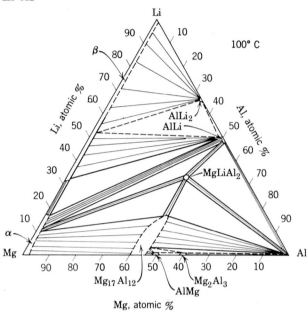

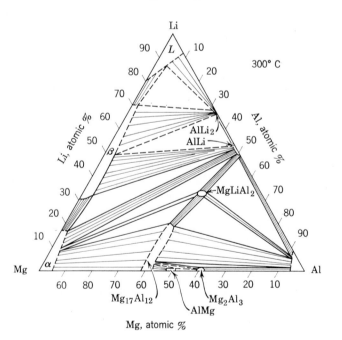

# Mg-Li-Al (Cont.)

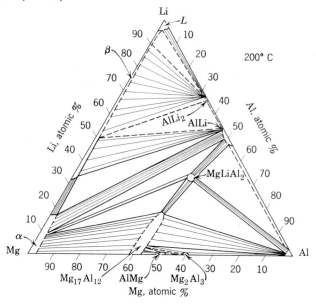

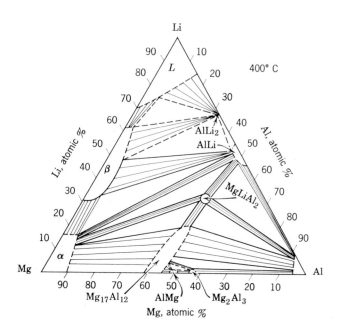

The latest complete study of this sytem was published by D. W. Levinson and D. J. McPherson, *Trans. ASM*, **48,** 689 (1956). The isothermal sections at 100, 200, 300, and 400°C are modified versions of their illustrations. The single ternary phase is of approximate composition MgLiAl$_2$. Although a complete structure determination has not been made, it is cubic with a lattice parameter of approximately 20.2 A. Over the range of 100–400°C, MgLiAl$_2$ can exist in equilibrium with magnesium-rich solid solution, AlLi, aluminum-rich solid solution, and Mg$_{17}$Al$_{12}$. AlLi is cubic B32 (NaTl type) with $a = 6.37$ A and 16 atoms/unit cell. A transition or metastable phase of approximate composition MgLi$_2$Al has been found in β-alloys (Mg-Li cubic) near the β/β + AlLi boundary when quenched from 400°C. This phase is discussed in connection with precipitation in Section 5.3.

The commercial promise for alloys in this system is large if the problems of (a) overaging with loss of ductility and (b) corrosion can be overcome.

## 3.31 Mg-Li-Zn

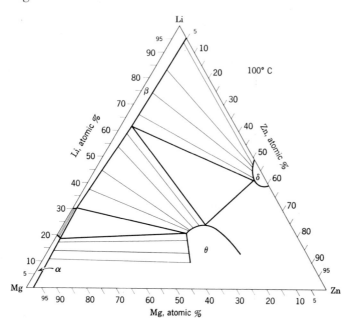

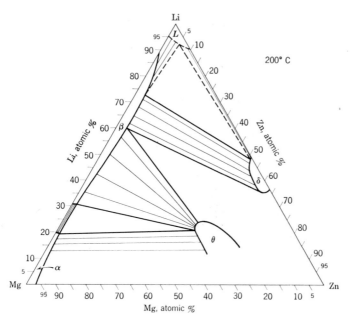

## Mg-Li-Zn (Cont.)

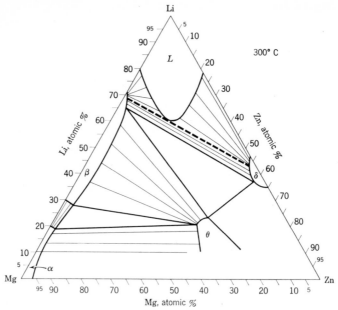

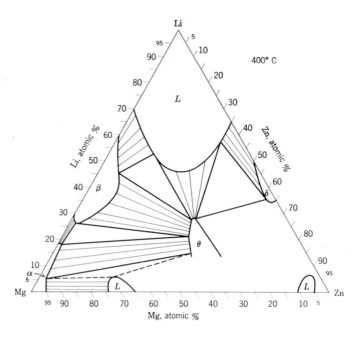

The accompanying isothermal sections are modified versions of the illustrations from the latest complete work on this system published by A. F. Weinberg, D. W. Levinson, and W. Rostoker, *Trans. ASM*, **48,** 855 (1956). Although the entire ternary range has not been studied, the central part of the system is the focus of interest and controversy. The only equilibrium ternary intermetallic phase is $\theta$, of approximate composition MgLiZn. Although the details of its structure are not known, it is cubic with a lattice parameter of 7.46 A. The $\theta$-phase can exist in equilibrium at least with magnesium-rich solid solution, $\beta$-phase (cubic Mg-Li) and LiZn. The latter is cubic B32 (NaTl type) with $a = 6.22$ A and 16 atoms/unit cell.

There is much evidence that a nonequilibrium phase of approximate stoichiometry MgLi$_2$Zn forms in the aging process in a complicated manner which will be discussed in Section 5.3. Some controversy remains on this point. Considerable commercial potential exists for alloys of this system if working, ductility, and corrosion problems can be controlled.

### 3.32  Mg-Th-Zn

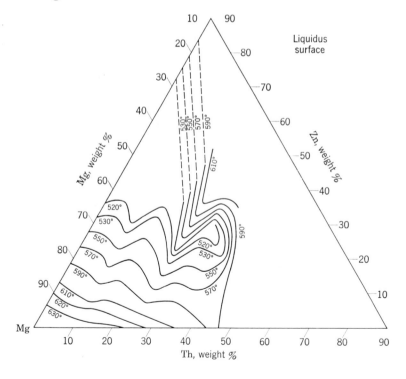

The liquidus surface in the magnesium-rich corner has been investigated by the Armour Research Foundation group. Isotherms in °C are shown in the diagram. The pronounced cooperative strengthening effect on magnesium of zinc and thorium gives this system great importance for both high- and normal-temperature applications. More complete knowledge of it depends somewhat upon resolution of controversies concerning the Mg-Zn and Mg-Th binary systems.

### 3.33  Mg-Th-Zr

A tentative vertical section of this system at 1% Zr and a segment of the probable liquidus surface have been published by Yamamoto and Rostoker (see reference in Section 3.24). Much more work is needed before reasonably complete diagrams can be constructed. This system has great commercial importance in magnesium alloys for high-temperature applications.

# 4

# The Deformation
# of
# Magnesium

## 4.1  Elastic and Anelastic Deformation

Five elastic constants are necessary to define the behavior of magnesium, a hexagonal crystal. The adiabatic constants, $C_{ij}$, at 298°K have been measured with ultrasonic pulse techniques by Long and Smith [1] and Slutsky and Garland.[2] Their results are presented in Table 4.1. Earlier measurements by Goens and Schmid [3] and Bridgman,[4] which differed considerably from these values have not been included. Also in Table 4.1 are the values of the adiabatic compliances, $S_{ij}$, the isothermal constants, $C_{ij}{}^{T}$, and the isothermal compliances, $S_{ij}{}^{T}$, as calculated by Long and Smith from their measurements. The nearly isotropic elasticity of magnesium is shown by the near identity of $(C_{11}-C_{12})$ to $2C_{44}$ and of $C_{33}$ to $C_{11}$. Slutsky and Garland [2] have reported the elastic constants and the calculated reciprocal compressibility for pure

Table 4.1.*   The Elastic Constants of Magnesium at 298°K [1,2]

| $ij$ | $C_{ij}$ | | $S_{ij}$ | $C_{ij}{}^{T}$ | $S_{ij}{}^{T}$ |
|------|----------|--------|----------|----------------|----------------|
| 11 | 0.5974 [1] | 0.5943 [2] | 2.200 | 0.5852 | 2.210 |
| 33 | 0.617 | 0.6164 | 1.971 | 0.605 | 1.983 |
| 44 | 0.1639 | 0.1642 | 6.101 | 0.1639 | 6.101 |
| 12 | 0.2624 | 0.256 | −0.786 | 0.2502 | −0.775 |
| 13 | 0.217 | 0.214 | −0.497 | 0.205 | −0.486 |

* In units of $10^{12}$ dynes/cm² for $C$ and $10^{-12}$ cm²/dyne for $S$.

Table 4.2.*    The Elastic Constants and the Calculated Reciprocal
Compressibility, $1/k = (2C_{11} + C_{33} + 2C_{12} + 4C_{13})/9$ of
Magnesium as a Function of Temperature [2]

| $T, °K$ | $C_{11}$ | $C_{33}$ | $C_{44}$ | $C_{12}$ | $C_{13}$ | $1/k$ |
|---|---|---|---|---|---|---|
| 0 | 0.6348 | 0.6645 | 0.1842 | 0.2594 | 0.2170 | 0.3689 |
| 20 | 0.6340 | 0.6640 | 0.1840 | 0.2594 | 0.2170 | 0.3688 |
| 40 | 0.6330 | 0.6635 | 0.1835 | 0.2593 | 0.2169 | 0.3684 |
| 60 | 0.6315 | 0.6616 | 0.1829 | 0.2592 | 0.2169 | 0.3676 |
| 80 | 0.6300 | 0.6595 | 0.1820 | 0.2591 | 0.2168 | 0.3669 |
| 100 | 0.6275 | 0.6566 | 0.1810 | 0.2590 | 0.2167 | 0.3659 |
| 120 | 0.6249 | 0.6534 | 0.1798 | 0.2588 | 0.2166 | 0.3650 |
| 140 | 0.6219 | 0.6495 | 0.1783 | 0.2586 | 0.2165 | 0.3638 |
| 160 | 0.6189 | 0.6455 | 0.1768 | 0.2585 | 0.2163 | 0.3630 |
| 180 | 0.6154 | 0.6411 | 0.1750 | 0.2582 | 0.2162 | 0.3614 |
| 200 | 0.6118 | 0.6370 | 0.1732 | 0.2580 | 0.2160 | 0.3603 |
| 220 | 0.6084 | 0.6326 | 0.1715 | 0.2576 | 0.2157 | 0.3590 |
| 240 | 0.6049 | 0.6281 | 0.1697 | 0.2573 | 0.2155 | 0.3574 |
| 260 | 0.6011 | 0.6243 | 0.1678 | 0.2569 | 0.2152 | 0.3556 |
| 280 | 0.5974 | 0.6200 | 0.1659 | 0.2565 | 0.2148 | 0.3537 |
| 300 | 0.5940 | 0.6160 | 0.1640 | 0.2561 | 0.2144 | 0.3524 |

* Values are taken from smooth curves in units of $10^{12}$ dynes/cm².

magnesium over the temperature range from 0° to 300°K. These results
appear in Table 4.2. The values in Table 4.2 were taken from smoothed
curves by the authors.

Polycrystalline magnesium is characterized by the bulk elastic properties which are based on isotropic elasticity theory. These are the average elastic modulus or Young's modulus, $E$, the compressibility, $k$, and
Poisson's ratio, $\nu$.

The static elastic moduli at several temperatures for magnesium of
two different purities have been determined by Fenn.[5] These results,
which were obtained from a 0.5-inch-diameter extruded rod, appear in
Table 4.3. Dynamic elastic moduli were obtained with the same mate-

rial at two of these temperatures by Graft and Levinson.[6] Their results also are shown in Table 4.3. From these data it can be seen that:

(a) The elastic moduli are dependent on the purity of the magnesium.
(b) The moduli decrease with increasing temperature.
(c) The elevated temperature decrease of static moduli is much greater than that of dynamic moduli.

It is known from the work of Kê [7] on polycrystalline magnesium, that (c) results from an anelastic effect of grain boundaries. The static test allows complete grain boundary strain relaxation, whereas the dynamic test permits such relaxation to occur only partially or not at all. This same effect occurs in some commercial magnesium alloys.

The compressibility of magnesium has been measured by Bridgman.[8, 9] He found a continuous decrease in its value as the hydrostatic stress increased. The initial value is as follows:

$$k_0 = \frac{1}{V}\left(\frac{dV}{dP}\right)_{P=0} = 2.0 \times 10^{-4} \text{ in.}^2/\text{lb} = 0.28 \text{ mm}^2/\text{kg}$$

Poisson's ratio for magnesium is almost universally quoted as 0.35, although there appears to be no publication of a careful direct measurement of it.

**Table 4.3. Elastic Moduli of Two Purities as a Function of Temperature in Units of $10^6$ psi [5, 6]**

| Temperature | | High-Purity Sublimed Magnesium ($1.7 \times 10^{-3}$ in. grain size) | Commercial Electrolytic Magnesium ($8 \times 10^{-4}$ in. grain size) |
|---|---|---|---|
| °F | °C | | |
| 78 | 26 | 5.77 | 6.24 |
| | | 6.16 (dynamic) | 6.53 (dynamic) |
| 200 | 93 | 5.18 | 5.33 |
| 300 | 149 | 4.82 | 4.65 |
| 400 | 204 | 4.90 | 3.87 |
| 500 | 260 | 4.85 | 3.21 |
| 600 | 316 | 4.36 | 2.40 |
| | | 5.41 (dynamic) | 5.79 (dynamic) |

## 4.2  Plastic Deformation by Slip

Progress in recognizing, rationalizing, and measuring appropriate stress and temperature dependence of deformation mechanisms in magnesium may be divided into three consecutive stages.  First, $\{10\bar{1}2\}$ $\langle10\bar{1}1\rangle$ twinning and (0001) $\langle11\bar{2}0\rangle$ slip at room temperature supplemented by $\{10\bar{1}1\}$ $\langle11\bar{2}0\rangle$ slip at elevated temperature were recognized in the 1930's and early 1940's.  The second period involved the examination of polycrystalline deformation and the attempts to rationalize finite ductility of the aggregate in terms of grain boundary shearing and general nonuniformities, accepting the limited number of crystallographic mechanisms above.  The third period, not yet complete, features discovery in both polycrystalline aggregates and the single crystal of many new twinning and slip mechanisms, the interplay of which varies with temperature.  The onset of fracture and the true role of cracking are understood more thoroughly now.  Magnesium has become a very interesting metal from the standpoint of crystallographic deformation mechanisms.

Slip may be defined macroscopically as the irreversible shear of part of a crystal with respect to another under shear stress without the breaking of a large number of interatomic bonds (fracture) or crystallographic reorientation (twinning).  Even if nothing were known about the actual slip mechanism in magnesium, certain theoretical predictions are possible if dislocation movement is assumed to cause all slip.  The shortest slip vector which preserves the ABAB basal or close-packed plane stacking is of magnitude $a$ and direction $\langle11\bar{2}0\rangle$.  The total strain energy is lowered by the dissociation in the basal plane of the dislocation into two partial dislocations having the slip vector $a/3$ $\langle10\bar{1}0\rangle$.[10]  A stacking fault exists in a narrow ribbon between the two partials.  The separation of these partials is controlled by the stacking-fault energy $\gamma$.  The decrease of energy in the dislocation strain field which results from dissociation is just balanced by the stacking-fault energy in the equilibrium case.  Although no direct way of measuring the fault energy is available for magnesium, Seeger estimates it to be in the range 200–400 ergs/cm.[11]  This leads to a predicted separation of the partials at room temperature of the order of an interatomic distance.

If these estimates are reasonably accurate, the stabilization of dislocation lines in the basal plane as a result of its dissociation into partials is a real but marginal effect.  One might expect, as is observed, that with increasing temperature thermal activation of the process of reforming the total dislocation (constriction) would allow escape of dislocations from the basal plane. Without the benefit of the stacking-fault ribbon, the resulting nonbasal slip occurs in slightly wavy lines, as expected.

The fine, extremely straight lines of slip in the basal plane are easily observable after deformation on previously polished surfaces of magnesium. They are more difficult to identify the purer the magnesium and the higher the temperature of deformation. Their remarkable straightness in all cases probably results from the slight stabilization that the dissociation into partials affords in a close-packed plane.

Small amounts of nonbasal slip are seen after room temperature deformation of pure magnesium, Figs. 4.1 and 4.2. The amount increases as the temperature is raised or lowered. The earliest observations of nonbasal slip were made by Schmid,[12] who concluded that the $\{10\bar{1}1\}$ $\langle 11\bar{2}0 \rangle$ system became operative at 225°C and above. Later work on the compression of thin single-crystal wafers by Bakarian and Mathewson [13] confirmed the significance of this temperature, and contributed the first extensive evidence on the waviness of elevated-temperature slip lines on this system. Using high-purity single crystals in tension, Burke and Hibbard observed basal slip to be the only system

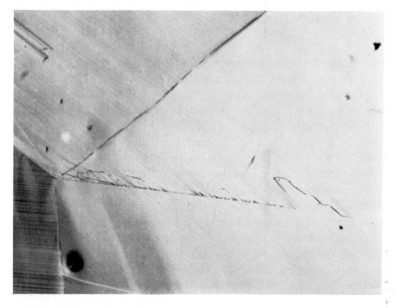

Fig. 4.1. $\{10\bar{1}0\}$ $<11\bar{2}0>$ slip in polycrystalline pure magnesium after 0.85% plastic strain in tension at 25°C. Stress axis vertical, 150✕.

Fig. 4.2.  Nonbasal slip crossing basal slip in polycrystalline pure magnesium after 3% plastic strain in tension at 25°C.  Basal plane nearly parallel to stress axis, which is vertical, 50×.

operative at room temperature, except in one case.[14]   This particular crystal showed slip on the pyramidal or $\{10\bar{1}1\}$ $\langle 11\bar{2}0 \rangle$ system.  Since the resolved shear stress on this nonbasal system was higher than that on the basal system, the observation was rationalized in terms of grip constraint on the basal planes, which were at a small angle to the tensile stress axis.

Thus, up until 1955, there was an acceptance of 225°C as the temperature below which no slip system except (0001) $\langle 11\bar{2}0 \rangle$ would operate in magnesium without the imposition of unusual stress systems.  At about this time, Hauser, in the group led by Dorn at the University of California, began to examine rather critically the deformation in tension of polycrystalline pure magnesium.[15]  It soon became apparent that, at last in polycrystalline metal, the deformation mechanisms were considerably more complex than was generally supposed in the past.  Small amounts of nonbasal slip were seen at room temperature and, more important, the temperature dependence of nonbasal slip was found not to be as simple as had been thought before.  Hauser found that duplex slip on $\{10\bar{1}0\}$ planes occurred in conjunction with basal slip at low temperatures.[16]

At about the same time a re-examination of the deformation of single crystals also was being undertaken. This work was accomplished by Reed-Hill by studying tensile deformation with the stress axis close enough to the basal plane that basal slip and mechanical twinning on $\{10\bar{1}2\}$ were suppressed.[17] This orientation is of considerable practical significance in the tensile deformation of polycrystalline sheet and ex- truded metal because of the preferred orientation. Reed-Hill strained crystals at $-190°$, $25°$, $150°$ and $286°C$. He found that $\{10\bar{1}0\}$ $\langle11\bar{2}0\rangle$ slip occurred at $-190°$ and $25°C$. At low temperature the slip lines had a minimum spacing of less than $5 \times 10^{-5}$ cm. Fine lines were seen to be cross-slipped by basal slip at both of these temperatures. These results are in excellent agreement with those of Hauser et al. at the low temperature.

At the elevated temperatures, Reed-Hill found that with the geometry of his crystals the slip lines were so irregular and diffuse that direct trace analysis of their system was not possible. However, a careful study of the asterisms in Laue x-ray photograms made from the deformed crystals showed them to be interpretable as the result of predominantly $\{10\bar{1}1\}$ $\langle11\bar{2}0\rangle$ pyramidal slip. There appears to be no conflict between these results and those of Schmid and Bakarian, except that the signifi- cance of the $225°C$ temperature is lost.

The high-temperature deformation of magnesium has also been in- vestigated by Chaudhuri et al., who used very coarse-grained polycrys- talline specimens in tensile creep at $500°F$ $(260°C)$.[18, 19] At rather slow strain rates, they found from a careful trace analysis that, although the $\langle11\bar{2}0\rangle$ directions were invariant, the apparent slip planes were neither $\{10\bar{1}1\}$ nor $\{10\bar{1}0\}$ in most cases. Rather, they fell closest to the plane of maximum resolved shear stress between these two planes. This ob- servation coupled with the waviness of the bands of slip led them to sug- gest a cooperative process in which slip would occur with microscopic alternation on prism and pyramidal planes.

These results and the qualifications of Reed-Hill concerning identifi- cation of the elevated temperature systems, as well as his observation of short, disconnected lines of noncrystallographic slip at $-190°$ and $25°C$, illustrate that the interplay of the slip systems is basically complex.

The alloying of $4.6\%$ (14.5 atomic $\%$) lithium to magnesium allows the operation of large amounts of prismatic $\{10\bar{1}0\}$ $\langle11\bar{2}0\rangle$ slip according to the work of Hauser et al.[20] Ductility is increased and strain-hardening is reduced markedly over magnesium and other binary alloys in the tem- perature range of $78°-298°K$. These investigators associate the intro- duction of the prismatic slip system with the pronounced decrease of the $c/a$ ratio from 1.624 in pure magnesium to 1.610 in the alloy. This association harmonizes with the trend of slip-system importance as a function of $c/a$ ratio in the hexagonal metals as a group.

Reed-Hill has reported $\{11\bar{2}2\}$ slip "bands" on magnesium single crystals which were tested at $-190°C$.[21] There are indications that the slip direction is $\langle 10\bar{1}0 \rangle$.

There has not yet been any fully confirmed evidence of slip in metallic crystals with other than the most closely packed direction in the crystal as the slip direction. If it is assumed that such slip is either impossible or of negligible importance, an interesting comparison may be made between the cubic metals and magnesium. The cubic metals may, in principle, deform by slip alone, since their crystal symmetry allows several noncoplanar slip directions. The close-packed or $\langle 11\bar{2}0 \rangle$ directions in magnesium, which are the only confirmed slip directions, lie all in the basal plane of the crystal. Thus, in polycrystalline magnesium, even though many slip planes or noncrystallographic slip operates, plastic deformation is not possible, in principle, from slip in the $\langle 11\bar{2}0 \rangle$ directions alone. However, considerable plasticity is observed. The results of many studies of the complexity of magnesium deformation show that, fortunately for the structural applications of the metal, several other mechanisms supplement that of simple slip. They are cell formation, twinning, compression banding, and grain boundary deformation.

The formation of a substructure of cells of subgrains within a magnesium grain is somewhat allied to the basal slip process. Such cell formation appears to be a complication of the simple aggregation of dislocations into arrays by glide and climb in the single crystal. Cell formation has been observed in polycrystalline magnesium and magnesium alloys.[22-24] Its operation near grain boundaries is especially pronounced.

### 4.3   Plastic Deformation by Twinning

Magnesium twins mechanically on $\{10\bar{1}2\}$, $\{30\bar{3}4\}$, $\{10\bar{1}3\}$, $\{11\bar{2}4\}$, and perhaps on $\{10\bar{1}1\}$, $\{10\bar{1}4\}$, $\{10\bar{1}5\}$, and $\{11\bar{2}1\}$. More experimental confirmation is merited for all but the $\{10\bar{1}2\}$ twinning, which is so easily recognized that its importance in deformation of the metal was realized early. Its operation can be detected by the "crackling" which sounds when a single crystal or recrystallized bar of polycrystalline pure magnesium is bent. The boundaries of lenticular $\{10\bar{1}2\}$ twins are easily etched in metallographic sectioning, as shown in Fig. 4.3. This photomicrograph also shows second-order twins and $\{10\bar{1}2\}$ twin intersections of several types. The producer of sheet magnesium encounters $\{10\bar{1}2\}$ twinning when the sheet is found to be shorter and thicker after roller leveling (straightening between rolls). The reason for these dimensional

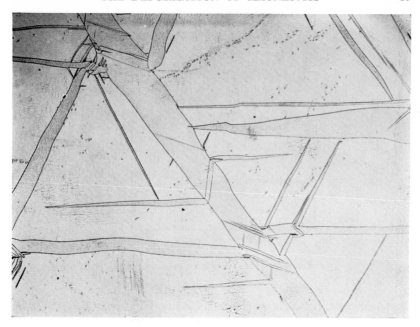

Fig. 4.3. Complex of {10$\bar{1}$2} twins in deformed, pure-magnesium single crystal, surface near basal plane. Note second-order twins and twin intersections. (Courtesy of R. E. Reed-Hill.)

changes is apparent in Fig. 4.4 which shows the shear strain (0.131) and one possible direction, [$\bar{1}$011] of the family ⟨10$\bar{1}$1⟩, for {10$\bar{1}$2} twinning in magnesium. When the atoms above the twinning plane move into the mirror positions across it with respect to those below it, an over-all increase in length occurs in the $c$ direction and a decrease occurs in the $a$ direction. This is a simple geometrical result of the angle between {10$\bar{1}$2} and (0001), 43° 9', being less than 45°.

Barrett has made an analysis of atom movements in {10$\bar{1}$2} hexagonal twinning.[25] The hexagonal close-packed structure is such that only one-half of the atoms forming the twin can move in simple homogeneous shear (parallel to the twinning plane). The others move in various directions. There are four conceivable sets of atom movements. Barrett concludes that one is the most probable, since it avoids the abnormally small interatomic distances at the interface which are characteristic of the other three.

It can be said that {10$\bar{1}$2} twinning is favored by compression parallel to the basal plane and tension perpendicular to it. The development of

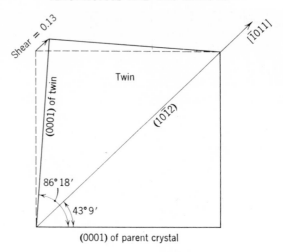

Fig. 4.4. $\{10\bar{1}2\}$ twinning in magnesium.

the single-crystal orientation criterion for the operation of different twinning systems has been discussed by Frank and Thompson.[26]  After hot-rolling or cold-rolling plus annealing, recrystallized magnesium alloy sheet is composed of grains more or less near to the "ideal" orientation, i.e., one with the c axis perpendicular to the surface.  Details of the rolling texture and the real deviations from this ideal are discussed in Chapter 7.  However, the thickening of sheet after bending operations can be explained here by applying the single-crystal orientation criterion to the "ideal" texture.

The single-crystal orientation criterion is not very reliably applied to individual grains in an aggregate subject to known macroscopic stresses. In cases where twinning has been found to occur in opposition to over-all macrostresses, it contributes a strain which is negative to the over-all plastic strain.[15]

The complete formation of a twin under conditions where the parent crystal has no restraint to the resulting shear is a simple case, not usually met in practice.  In general, accommodation to the shear is accomplished by a phenomenon known as accommodation kinking.  The plane of accommodation is usually called a *bend plane* or *kink plane*.  Accommodation may be expected on both $\{10\bar{1}0\}$ and $\{11\bar{2}0\}$ planes, as has been observed in magnesium.

The temperature dependence of $\{10\bar{1}2\}$ twinning has never been studied thoroughly under conditions where the variables of strain rate and orientation were fixed.  Twinning in polycrystalline magnesium becomes less important at elevated temperatures, but whether this is intrinsic to the twinning mechanism or not cannot be said, since the critical stresses for nonbasal slip and grain boundary deformation decrease rapidly with increasing temperature.

The existence of an apparently twinned structure on the habit of $\{30\bar{3}4\}$ was reported from the studies of deformed polycrystalline magnesium specimens.[27, 28] High-magnification photographs of this perplexing structure were published by Hauser et al.[15] and by Roberts in discussion of their paper. After identification of the habit as $\{30\bar{3}4\}$ by Couling and Roberts [28] from studies of deformed polycrystalline magnesium alloy, confirmation was obtained on single crystals by Reed-Hill.[29] These twins are uniquely narrow and they form in what Reed-Hill calls "bands." These bands form interesting arrays at low strain levels, as shown in Fig. 4.5. At high magnifications, they appear to be deformed to a great extent by slip or second-order twinning shortly after they have formed, Fig. 4.6. The important role which these twins play in limiting microscopic ductility is described in Section 4.7. Despite the neatness of the identification as $\{30\bar{3}4\}$ twinning, several inconsistencies have remained in the evidence concerning this structure, however. The

Fig. 4.5. Array of $\{30\bar{3}4\}$ twins in polycrystalline pure magnesium after 6% plastic strain in tension at 25°C. Stress axis vertical, 100✕.

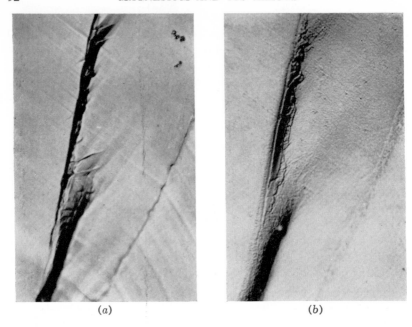

(a)                              (b)

Fig. 4.6. Highly deformed $\{30\bar{3}4\}$ twin in polycrystalline pure magnesium after (a) 2% plastic strain in tension at 25°C and (b) repolishing electrolytically. Stress axis vertical, 500×.

proposition of the twinning elements $K_1$, $\eta_1$, $K_2$, and $\eta_2$ as $\{30\bar{3}4\}$, $\langle 20\bar{2}3\rangle$, $(0001)$, and $\langle 10\bar{1}0\rangle$ respectively, as given by Couling and Roberts,[28] leads to a predicted shear of 1.422 which would occur when tension was applied *parallel* to the c axis. The results of Reed-Hill show that this structure is formed invariably when tension is applied *perpendicular* to the c axis. Reed-Hill proposes that the twinning elements are $\{30\bar{3}4\}$, $\langle 20\bar{2}3\rangle$, $\{10\bar{1}2\}$, and $\langle 10\bar{1}1\rangle$. These elements are chosen to account for the shear measured from the tilt of a surface parallel to the basal plane. However, it has not been possible to derive a crystallographic model of simple twinning to fit both these elements and the relatively small shear of 0.27 which Reed-Hill measured. According to Reed-Hill, these difficulties are related to the complicated kinks which almost always accompany these twins.[30] At the present, a final conclusion on this mechanism cannot be reached.

Twinning on $\{10\bar{1}1\}$,[12] $\{10\bar{1}3\}$, $\{11\bar{2}4\}$, $\{10\bar{1}4\}$, $\{10\bar{1}5\}$,[31] as well as on $\{11\bar{2}1\}$,[28] awaits further study and confirmation.

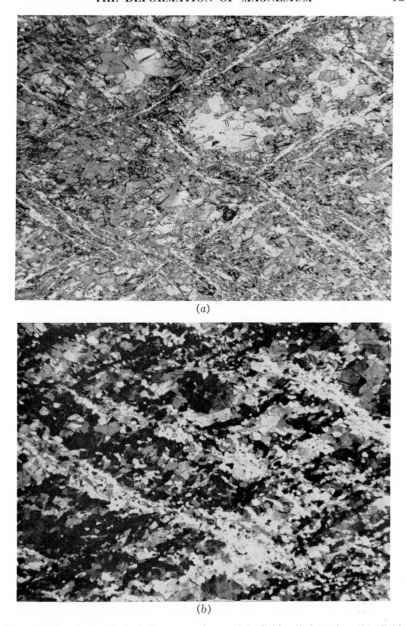

(a)

(b)

Fig. 4.7. Bands in electrolytic magnesium.   (a) Cold-rolled 50%.   (b) Cold-rolled 50% and annealed 1 min at 400°F.[34]   Acetic picral etch.   Polarized light through blue interference filter, 100×.

## 4.4   Compression Banding

An important feature of the microstructure of magnesium and its alloys, after primarily compressive deformation, is the existence of material in bands which are symmetrically inclined to the plane normal to the compression axis. These bands have been observed in compression specimens and rolled sheet by several investigators.[32-35]

This banding was first explained by Ernst and Laves as the result of cracking and rewelding.[36]   Later work appeared to support this view.[37] Examples are shown in Figs. 4.7 and 4.8.   Recently, it has been suggested [35] that the explanation of Ernst and Laves is incorrect and that bands are formed by a complex double-twinning mechanism (a $\{10\bar{1}1\}$ twin forms first and the twinned material retwins on a $\{10\bar{1}2\}$ plane).

A modification of the orientation-sensitive etching and polarized-light method of Ernst and Laves made by Couling and Pearsall [38] has permitted a rather complete study of these bands.   Couling has found that the basal plane has been reoriented into near parallelism with the planes of the bands.[34]   The importance of this correlation in understanding the preferred orientation of wrought magnesium alloys is discussed in Chapter 7.   Material reorientation during band formation allows later basal slip within the band to bring the orientation of the basal plane into complete parallelism with it.   This interpretation of the banding phenomenon is especially useful in explaining the anomalous rolling behavior of certain magnesium alloys that are also discussed in Section 7.6.

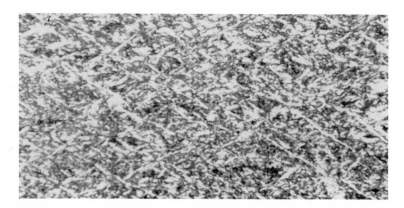

Fig. 4.8.   Bands in a magnesium-0.5% thorium alloy after cold-rolling 87%.[35] Acetic picral etch.   Polarized light through blue filter, 150✕.

## 4.5   Grain Boundary Deformation

The anelastic behavior of grain boundaries described in Section 4.1 has its plastic counterpart in magnesium as well as in other metals. The operation of grain boundary shearing under tension at room temperature was proved in the polycrystalline aggregate by Hauser et al.[15] The importance of the process in the creep of polycrystalline magnesium at elevated temperatures has been demonstrated by Couling and Roberts.[39] They found that high-temperature grain boundary deformation in a simple polycrystalline magnesium aggregate is a two-stage process involving alternate boundary shearing and migration. Increasing test temperatures and decreasing strain rates favor larger contributions to the over-all strain from boundary deformation. In the limiting case, it appears that all the deformation would be localized at the boundaries. A mechanism which explains the observations is the alternation of anelastic boundary shears with the *capture* of these shears when the boundaries migrate to new positions. The number of cycles necessary to produce the measured shear on a simple boundary has been calculated and found to agree qualitatively with metallographic observation.

## 4.6   The Phenomenology of Plastic Deformation

The contrast in behavior between the single crystal and the polycrystalline aggregate of unalloyed magnesium is great. Large amounts of ductility and a relatively low rate of strain-hardening are observed over a wide temperature range for the single crystal, whereas severe limitations on ductility and a pronounced increase in both strength and strain-hardening are found for polycrystalline specimens. The same understanding of the practical behavior of magnesium alloys in structural applications results from a study of this contrast. The behavior both in tension and in shear of a magnesium single crystal may be idealized as follows. The small elastic strain is essentially independent of the orientation because of the nearly isotropic elasticity of magnesium, but will be dependent on temperature to the degree shown in Table 4.3. The plastic deformation begins at the yield stress, $\sigma_0$, which may be resolved into a critical shear stress on the active slip plane, $\tau_0$. It proceeds with a constant strain-hardening rate given by a strain-hardening coefficient, $h$, until fracture occurs. Some single-crystal stress-strain curves obtained by Conrad [40] at several temperatures, Fig. 4.9, conform rather well to the idealized behavior. The contrast with these curves are those

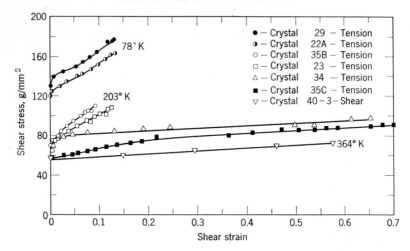

Fig. 4.9.  Stress-strain curves of pure-magnesium single crystals at 78°, 203°, and 364° K according to Conrad and Robertson.[40]

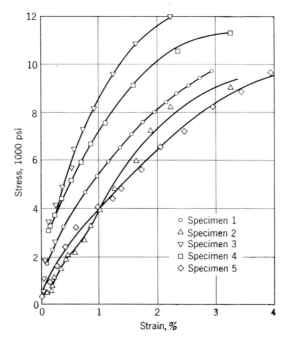

Fig. 4.10.  Stress-strain curves for polycrystalline pure magnesium at room temperature according to Hauser et al.[15]

obtained by Hauser et al.,[15] from polycrystalline metal of equivalent purity at room temperature, Fig. 4.10. The restriction of magnesium to a grain size of about 1 mm increases the yield stress by a factor of ten or more, increases the strain-hardening rate by more than a factor of $10^3$, and reduces the fracture strain tenfold. (In comparing these curves, it is helpful to remember that 1 psi equals about 0.7 g/mm$^2$.) This is, of course, very different from the behavior of cubic metals, where the single-crystal and polycrystalline pure-metal stress-strain curves are not greatly different.

The concept of a critical resolved shear stress for slip has been applied historically to magnesium as well as to other metals. Those who have studied the deformation of single crystals have measured values of this parameter for the (0001) $\langle 11\bar{2}0 \rangle$, $\{10\bar{1}1\}$, and $\{10\bar{1}0\}$ $\langle 11\bar{2}0 \rangle$ slip systems. These values are summarized in Table 4.4. Although the table is by no means complete, there are enough data to indicate by systematic trends in critical resolved shear stress with temperature that the parameter has some significance. However, the stress-strain curves from which these values are obtained and the methods of obtaining them by extrapolation should be examined critically before these values are used quantita-

Table 4.4.  Critical Resolved Shear Stresses (g/mm$^2$) for Slip in Magnesium as Determined in Tension by Various Investigators *

| System | −190°C | 25°C | 150°C | 286°C |
|---|---|---|---|---|
| (0001) $\langle 11\bar{2}0 \rangle$, basal | | S 83 BM 78 BH 46 HC 66 CR 53 | | BM 66 |
| $\{10\bar{1}1\}$ $\langle 11\bar{2}0 \rangle$, pyramidal | | BH 52 | R 1400 | BM 400 R 110 |
| $\{10\bar{1}0\}$ $\langle 11\bar{2}0 \rangle$, prismatic | R 10,000 | R 4000 | R 1600 | R 130 |

* S—Schmid;[12] BM—Bakarian and Mathewson;[13] BH—Burke and Hibbard;[14] HC—Hsu and Cullity;[41] R—Reed-Hill;[17] CR—Conrad and Robertson.[40]

tively.  The decrease of the room temperature value for the basal system with successive investigations may be connected with the refinement of measurement systems.

As a result of an extensive study of the effect of temperature on the plastic flow of magnesium single crystals, Conrad came to the conclusion that none of the existing formal theories of plastic flow were satisfactory for the behavior of magnesium.  He described his results with the following empirical equation:

$$\dot{\gamma} = C \exp \left( \frac{-\Delta H}{RT} \right) \exp B(\tau - h\gamma)$$

where $\gamma$ is the strain, $\tau$ is the applied stress, $R$ is the gas constant, $T$ is the absolute temperature, $\Delta H$ is the activation energy (10.3 kcal/g-atom), and $B$ and $C$ are constants.

The strain-hardening coefficient was found to be independent of the previous strain history.  However, it decreases rapidly with increasing

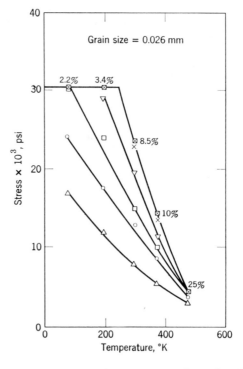

Fig. 4.11.  Flow and fracture stress for pure magnesium of grain size 0.026 mm as a function of temperature according to Hauser et al.[42]

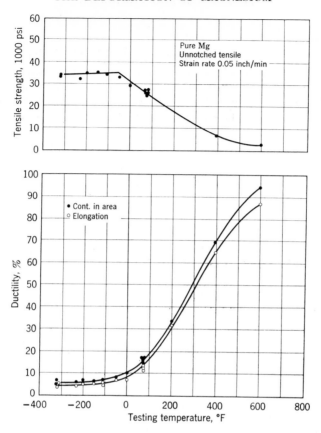

Fig. 4.12. Tensile properties of pure magnesium of approximate grain size 0.03 mm as a function of temperature according to Toaz and Ripling.[43]

temperature in the vicinity of room temperature. This decrease is believed to be the classical thermal recovery of strain-hardening. The magnitude of the recovery at such low temperatures is important in the understanding of the behavior of polycrystalline magnesium as well as its alloys. Magnesium crystals are *completely* recovered after large strains by heating for 1 to 2 hr at 450°C.

The tensile characteristics of high-purity polycrystalline magnesium have been developed as a function of temperature, grain size, and strain rate. Useful parameters that have been used to summarize many isothermal stress-strain curves are the flow and fracture stresses. These are the stresses at specified strains and at fracture. (The fracture con-

cept is not simple in itself. More is presented on this topic in Section
4.7.) The data of Hauser et al.,[42] Fig. 4.11, agree rather well in trend
with those of Toaz and Ripling,[43] Fig. 4.12. They both show that fine-
grained magnesium fractures at low but rather constant stress in the
temperature range below about 250°K. Above this range, the fracture
stress decreases rapidly with increasing temperature, and the ductility
increases markedly. The temperature at which this change occurs is regarded by Hauser et al. as a transition point from brittle to ductile
fracture. However, they emphasize that, even at the lowest test temperatures, some plastic deformation precedes fracture. Several grain
sizes were studied, and the transition temperature increased with increasing grain size, as shown in Fig. 4.13. The brittle or low-temperature stress increased linearly with the reciprocal square root of the grain
size over the range of 0.02–1 mm grain size, in accordance with the classical brittle-fracture law. Both groups of investigators found the low-
temperature fracture stress as well as the fracture strain relatively
independent of the strain rate over the range $10^{-4} - 1/\text{min}$. The interpretation by Toaz and Ripling of the discontinuities in Figs. 4.11, 4.12,
and 4.13 is somewhat different from that of Hauser et al. The former
investigators reserve the use of the term *transition temperature* for the

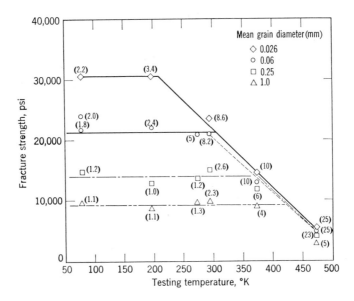

Fig. 4.13. Effect of temperature and grain size on the fracture strength of polycrystalline pure magnesium according to Hauser et al.[42]

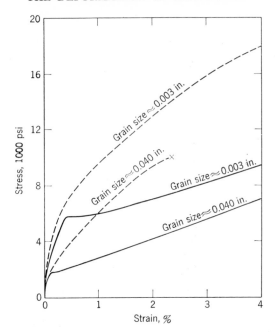

Fig. 4.14. Stress-strain curves for polycrystalline pure magnesium at 25°C. Compressive curves in solid, tensile curves in dashed line. (Courtesy, The Dow Chemical Company.)

situation where a change from brittle to ductile behavior occurs with no thermal instability of the microstructure, and where negligible deformation occurs prior to fracture in the brittle range. On the basis of some metallographic studies, they conclude that the discontinuities in the case of pure magnesium result from the entrance of recrystallization during the deformation. Thus they do not recognize magnesium as exhibiting a true brittle-to-ductile transition. Except for this, the difference between their description and that of Hauser et al. appears to be mainly one of semantics. The fact remains that the room temperature behavior of pure polycrystalline magnesium is essentially of the low temperature type, and that great improvements in its ductility result from an increase in deformation temperature or alloy content.

The tensile creep of fine-grained (0.1 mm grain size) electrolytic (not highest purity) magnesium has been investigated over the temperature range 200°–600°F.[23] The plastic creep strain is described by the summation of two components, one a transient, which is mainly associated with deformation within the grains, and the other a steady-state, which

is mainly associated with grain boundary deformation.[39]  The experimental data are fitted empirically on this basis to the relation:

$$\epsilon = 4.5 \times 10^{-9} \exp\left(\frac{-15{,}500}{RT}\right) \sigma^{4.0} t^{0.53} + k(\sigma^{b(T)}, T)t$$

where $\epsilon$ is the creep strain, $R$ is the gas constant, $\sigma$ is the stress in psi, $t$ is
the time in hours, $T$ is the absolute temperature, $k$ is a constant.

In discussion of this work,[44] it was pointed out that, if the constant in
the numerator of the exponential were converted to a kinetic base of $t^{-1}$,
the result of 29,000 kcal/g-atom, regarded as an activation energy, agrees
fairly well with the activation energy for self-diffusion of magnesium (see
Section 5.1).  This correlation for magnesium is similar to that which
has been performed for many metals.[45]  However, the situation is not
clarified by Conrad's report of an activation energy of 10,500 kcal/g-
atom for single-crystal magnesium creep.[40]

Stress-strain curves for the compressive deformation of magnesium
are compared with tensile curves for the same material in Fig. 4.14.
The onset of plastic deformation, although at a lower stress level, is
sharper than is observed in the tensile case.  Also greater apparent ductility to fracture is observed than in the case of tension.

## 4.7  Ductility and Fracture

These topics are especially important to consider in any discussion of
the deformation of magnesium and its alloys, primarily because of the
frequent engineering misunderstanding of the metal in connection with
brittleness.  Magnesium, unfortunately, exhibits its poorest behavior
under the testing conditions most in vogue for material evaluation.  To
quote Toaz and Ripling: [43]

. . . the performance of these materials is not greatly harmed by adverse
straining conditions.  Actually, low testing temperatures and high strain rates
are not as damaging to these alloys as they are for most other non-face-centered-
cubic materials.  The greatest shortcoming of the magnesium base alloys appears
to be their moderate ductility under ideal straining conditions—slow, uniaxial
tension at room temperature.

The traditional definitions of ductility and fracture are not quite
sufficient for understanding the mechanism of the behavior of metals at
large strains.  Tensile ductility is normally taken as the strain or reduction in a cross-sectional area of a test specimen when it breaks completely
into pieces.  This breaking which occurs at the end of the ductility is
called fracture.  However, there is now ample evidence that polycrystalline magnesium and its alloys begin to crack microscopically in tension

at strains about one-half those at which separation of a test specimen occurs. It is quite possible that such behavior is general for polycrystalline metals.

Fracture in tension results when the microcracks which have been formed considerably earlier in the straining join together completely. The prime crack loci in magnesium and its alloys appear to be:

1. Grain boundaries. These are more important in the pure metal than in the alloys.[15, 16, 27] They also become more prominent sites of crack development or cavitation the higher the temperature.[46]

2. The twinned structures which have been identified as $\{30\bar{3}4\}$ twins. A good example of such fracture is shown in Fig. 4.15.

3. At room temperature and below on other high-order planes, such as $\{10\bar{1}4\}$ or $\{10\bar{1}5\}$ and $\{11\bar{2}4\}$.[31]

The fracture of magnesium and its alloys near and below room temperature results primarily from the joining of the intragranular cracks (on loci 2 and 3 above) by a moderate amount of intergranular cracking (locus 1). At elevated temperatures, the cracking and cavitation at grain boundaries become much more important. A qualitative explanation of the ductility and fracture-stress dependence on temperature may be made on the basis of the following premises:

1. The amount of plastic strain to the stage of initial cracking is determined by the number of plastic deformation mechanisms available at the stress level in effect.

2. The amount of plastic strain available after the start of cracking is controlled by the ease with which these cracks can join together at the operative stress level.

The rather rapid increase in ductility with increasing temperature in magnesium results from the increase in both (1) and (2). The increase in (1) results from the decreasing stress necessary to initiate nonbasal slip as temperature and grain boundary deformation increase. The decrease in fracture stress with increasing temperature in the ductile range results from this decreasing yield stress as well as from the occurrence of recovery and recrystallization to an increasing degree at the higher temperatures.

The formation of voids and cracks at strain levels well below actual macroscopic fracture has also been observed during creep of magnesium and alloys at constant stress. Some results of Pearsall,[47] Fig. 4.16, show that, although the tertiary stage of creep is associated with rapid increase in crack density, voids are being generated well before the increase in strain rate. However, in the case of a commercially creep-resistant alloy

Fig. 4.15.   Crack in {30$\bar{3}$4} twin formed in tensile deformation of polycrystalline pure magnesium at 25°C.

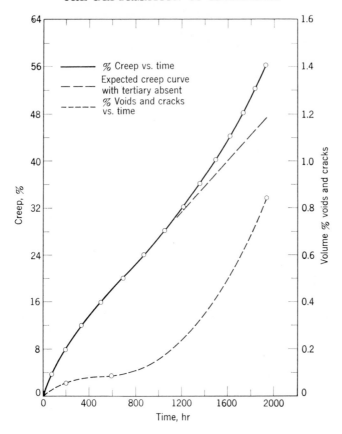

Fig. 4.16. Increase in voids and cracks during creep of polycrystalline pure magnesium at 300°F and 2000 psi.[47]

containing thorium and manganese, the rapidly increasing strain rate in tertiary creep at 600°F could not be ascribed primarily to either cracking or necking. A true softening of the metal, probably by recrystallization, appears to be involved.

## References

1. T. R. Long and C. S. Smith, "Single-Crystal Elastic Constants of Magnesium and Magnesium Alloys," *Acta Met.*, **5**, 200 (1957).
2. J. Slutsky and C. W. Garland, "Elastic Constants of Magnesium from 4.2°K to 300°K," *Phys. Rev.*, **107**, 972 (1957).
3. E. Goens and E. Schmid, "Elastische Konstanten, elektrischer Widerstand und thermische Ausdehnung," *Physik. Z.*, **37**, 385 (1936).

4. P. W. Bridgman, "Physical Properties of Single Crystal Magnesium," *Proc. Am. Acad. Arts Sci.*, **67**, 29 (1932).

5. R. W. Fenn, Jr., "Young's Modulus of Magnesium Alloys as a Function of Temperature and Metallurgical Variables," to be published by the ASTM.

6. W. H. Graft and D. W. Levinson, discussion of Reference 5.

7. T. S. Kê, "Experimental Evidence of the Viscous Behavior of Grain Boundaries in Metals," *Phys. Rev.*, **71**, 533 (1947).

8. P. W. Bridgman, "The Compression of 39 Substances to 100,000 kg/cm$^2$," *Proc. Am. Acad. Arts Sci.*, **76**, 55 (1948).

9. P. W. Bridgman, "The Linear Compression of Various Single Crystals to 30 kg/cm$^2$," *Proc. Am. Acad. Arts Sci.*, **76**, 89 (1948).

10. W. T. Read, Jr., *Dislocations in Crystals*, McGraw-Hill Book Co., New York 1953, Chapter 7.

11. A. Seeger, Report of *The Conference on Defects in Crystalline Solids*, The Physical Society, London, 1955, 328.

12. E. Schmid, "Beiträge zur Physik und Metallographie des Magnesiums," *Z. Elektrochem.*, **37**, 447 (1931).

13. P. W. Bakarian and C. H. Mathewson, "Slip and Twinning of Magnesium Single Crystals at Elevated Temperatures," *Trans. AIME*, **152**, 226 (1943).

14. E. C. Burke and W. R. Hibbard, Jr., "Plastic Deformation of Magnesium Single Crystals," *Trans. AIME*, **194**, 295 (1952).

15. F. E. Hauser, C. D. Starr, L. S. Tietz, and J. E. Dorn, "Deformation Mechanisms in Polycrystalline Aggregates of Magnesium," *Trans. ASM*, **47**, 102 (1955).

16. F. E. Hauser, P. R. Landon, and J. E. Dorn, "Deformation and Fracture Mechanisms of Polycrystalline Magnesium at Low Temperatures," *Trans. ASM*, **48**, 986 (1955).

17. R. E. Reed-Hill and W. D. Robertson, "Deformation of Magnesium Single Crystals by Non-basal Slip," *Trans. AIME*, **209**, 496 (1957).

18. A. R. Chaudhuri, N. J. Grant, and J. T. Norton, "Metallographic Observations of the Deformation of High-Purity Magnesium in Creep at 500°F," *Trans. AIME*, **197**, 712 (1953).

19. A. R. Chaudhuri, H. C. Chang, and N. J. Grant, "Creep Deformation of Magnesium at Elevated Temperature by Non-Basal Slip," *Trans. AIME*, **203**, 682 (1955).

20. F. E. Hauser, P. R. Landon, and J. E. Dorn, "Deformation and Fracture of Alpha Solid Solutions of Lithium in Magnesium," *Trans. ASM*, **50**, 856 (1958).

21. R. E. Reed-Hill and W. D. Robertson, "Pyramidal Slip in Magnesium," *Trans. AIME*, **212**, 256 (1958).

22. J. W. Suiter and W. A. Wood, "Deformation of Magnesium at Various Rates and Temperatures," *J. Inst. Metals*, **81**, 181 (1952).

23. C. S. Roberts, "Creep Behavior of Extruded Electrolytic Magnesium," *Trans. AIME*, **197**, 1121 (1953).

24. C. S. Roberts, "Creep Behavior of Magnesium-Cerium Alloys," *Trans. AIME*, **200**, 634 (1954).

25. C. S. Barrett, in *Cold Working of Metals*, American Society for Metals, Cleveland, 1949, pp. 78–86.

26. F. C. Frank and N. Thompson, "On Deformation by Twinning," *Acta Met.*, **3**, 30 (1955).
27. C. S. Roberts, "Non-Basal Slip and Twinning in Polycrystalline Magnesium at Room Temperature," *Wright Air Development Center Tech. Rept.*, No. 55-241 (1955).
28. S. L. Couling and C. S. Roberts, "New Twinning Systems in Magnesium," *Acta Cryst.*, **9**, 972 (1956).
29. R. E. Reed-Hill and W. D. Robertson, "Additional Modes of Deformation Twinning in Magnesium," *Acta Met.*, **5**, 717 (1957).
30. R. E. Reed-Hill (private communication).
31. R. E. Reed-Hill and W. D. Robertson, "The Crystallographic Characteristics of Fracture in Magnesium Single Crystals," *Acta Met.*, **5**, 728 (1957).
32. D. Grogan, *J. Inst. Metals,* **27**, 103 (1922). Discussion of F. Adcock, "The Internal Mechanism of Cold-Work and Recrystallization in Cupronickel," *Ibid.*, 73 (1922).
33. C. S. Roberts and E. C. Burke, "The Origin of the Double Peak in the Texture of Certain Rolled Magnesium Alloys," *Wright Air Development Center Tech. Rept.*, No. 55-160, Part 3 (1955).
34. S. L. Couling, "Investigation of Alloys of Magnesium and Their Properties," *Wright Air Development Center Tech. Rept.*, No. 57-194, Part 3 (1957).
35. S. L. Couling, J. F. Pashak, and L. Sturkey, "Unique Deformation and Aging Characteristics of Certain Magnesium-Base Alloys," *Trans. ASM,* **51**, 94 (1959).
36. T. Ernst and F. Laves, "The Deformation of Magnesium and Its Alloys," *Z. Metallk.*, **40**, 1 (1949).
37. F. Erdmann-Jesnitzer and H. Kahle, "Deformation of Polycrystalline Magnesium," *Metall.*, **9**, 776 (1955).
38. S. L. Couling and G. W. Pearsall, "Determination of Orientation in Magnesium by Polarized Light Examination," *Trans. AIME*, **209**, 939 (1957).
39. S. L. Couling and C. S. Roberts, "Grain Boundary Deformation in Fine-Grained Electrolytic Magnesium," *Trans. AIME*, **209**, 1252 (1957).
40. H. Conrad and W. D. Robertson, "Effect of Temperature on the Flow Stress and Strain-Hardening Coefficient of Magnesium Single Crystals," *Trans. AIME,* **209**, 503 (1957).
41. S. S. Hsu and B. D. Cullity, "On the Torsional Deformation and Recovery of Single Crystals," *Trans. AIME*, **200**, 305 (1954).
42. F. E. Hauser, P. R. Landon, and J. E. Dorn, "Fracture of Magnesium Alloys at Low Temperature," *Trans. AIME*, **206**, 589 (1956).
43. M. W. Toaz and E. J. Ripling, "Correlation of the Tensile Properties of Pure Magnesium and Four Commercial Alloys with Their Mode of Fracturing," *Trans. AIME,* **206**, 936 (1956).
44. O. D. Sherby and R. E. Frenkel, discussion of Reference 23.
45. J. E. Dorn, "The Spectrum of Activation Energies for the Creep of Metals," *Recovery and Creep,* American Society for Metals, Cleveland, 1957, 255.
46. J. N. Greenwood, D. R. Miller, and J. W. Suiter, "Intergranular Cavitation in Stressed Metals," *Acta Met.*, **2**, 250 (1954).
47. G. W. Pearsall (unpublished results), The Dow Chemical Company, Midland, Mich.

# 5

# Time-Temperature-
# Dependent Alloy
# Phenomena

## 5.1 Diffusion

The self-diffusion of magnesium was studied by Shewmon and Rhines,[1] who used polycrystalline extruded high-purity magnesium, the radioactive isotope $Mg^{28}$, and the sectioning technique. Radioactive magnesium was deposited on the surface of the specimens from the vapor phase. Concentration values were obtained from measurements of the radioactivity of the sections, which were cut parallel to the original interface with a lathe. They obtained the following values of the diffusion coefficient:

$$D = 4.4 \times 10^{-10} \text{ cm}^2/\text{sec} \quad \text{at } 468°C \ (741°K)$$

$$D = 3.6 \times 10^{-9} \text{ cm}^2/\text{sec} \quad \text{at } 551°C \ (824°K)$$

$$D = 2.1 \times 10^{-8} \text{ cm}^2/\text{sec} \quad \text{at } 627°C \ (900°K)$$

Their data were fitted well by the theoretical linear relation of the logarithm of the diffusion coefficient and the reciprocal of the absolute temperature. Such a plot led to the general relation:

$$D = 1.0 \exp \left(-32,000/RT\right) \text{ cm}^2/\text{sec}$$

The experimental value of the activation energy is in good agreement with the value of 30,500 cal/mole which is calculated from the Dushman-Langmuir equation.

The known preferred orientation of the magnesium extrusion from which the data above were obtained led the authors to realize that any anisotropy in the self-diffusivity of magnesium would influence their results. To determine the magnitude of any such anisotropy, similar experiments were performed on specimens from two single crystals, and the results were published by Shewmon.[2]  The $c$ axis in the two sets of specimens was at an angle of 7° and 78°, respectively, from the axis of diffusion.  The general relation for the diffusion coefficient in hexagonal crystals as a function of $D_\parallel$ and $D_\perp$, the diffusion coefficients parallel and perpendicular to the $c$ axis, respectively, and $\theta$, the angle between the diffusion axis and the $c$ axis is:

$$D(\theta) = D_\parallel \cos^2 \theta + D_\perp \sin^2 \theta$$

Combination of the final experimental results with this relation showed that the values of $D$ obtained from the two sets of specimens could be taken equal to $D_\parallel$ and $D_\perp$, respectively, with an error of less than 1%.

As in the study of polycrystalline specimens, the values of $D$ fitted the theoretical temperature dependence well.  The appropriate plots for $D_\parallel$, $D_\perp$, and the polycrystalline $D$ are presented in Fig. 5.1.  An anisotropy of self-diffusion does exist for magnesium.  This anisotropy may be expressed by the ratio $D_\perp/D_\parallel$ which has the following temperature dependence:

| Temperature, °C | $D_\perp/D_\parallel$ |
| --- | --- |
| 468 | 1.13 |
| 504 | 1.19 |
| 532.5 | 1.17 |
| 575.5 | 1.24 |

The larger value of $D_\perp$ is to be expected on the basis of the measurements on single-crystal thallium,[3] which has a $c/a$ ratio of 1.60 ($2\frac{1}{2}$% less than that for ideal close-packing, 1.633), and which showed the same direction of diffusion anisotropy.  The opposite is true for zinc [4] ($D_\parallel > D_\perp$), which has a $c/a$ ratio (1.86) much larger than the ideal.  However, this large anisotropy of self-diffusion is quite unexpected from a calculation of the deviation of magnesium from close-packing, which is less than 1%.  Shewmon assumes a vacancy mechanism on the reasonable basis of the evidence of mechanism in other metals.  He then derives an equation from random-walk theory and kinetic theory which relate $D_\perp/D_\parallel$ to the free energies of activation for diffusion in and out of the basal plane.  He shows from this equation that the diffusional anisotropy results from the entropy of activation being larger for diffusion perpendicular to the $c$ axis.  Consideration of the two saddle-point configurations and the sources of the entropy of activation for diffusion shows that this difference is reasonable.  It is believed to result primarily from

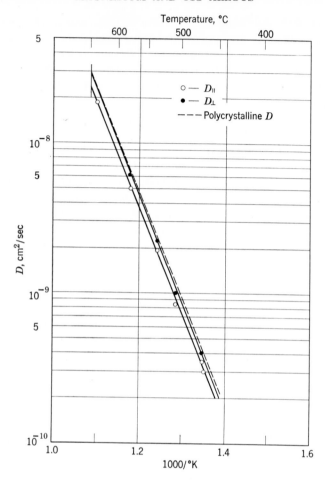

Fig. 5.1.　Temperature dependence of the self-diffusion coefficients of magnesium.[2]

the lower mean vibrational frequencies of the atoms at the saddle point for $D_\parallel$.

There has been no publication of the results of any systematic investigation of the diffusion of solute atoms in magnesium.

## 5.2　Recrystallization and Grain Growth

These phenomena are important in the practical working and annealing characteristics of magnesium and its alloys.　The term "hot-working" is most reasonably reserved for the deformation conditions where the metal is recrystallizing during the working process. Large reductions per pass in the rolling mill are possible with magnesium alloys under hot-working conditions, at 300°–450°C because of negligible work-hardening. "Cold-working," on the other hand, is most appropriately used to describe deformation in the absence of microscopically detectable recrystallization. One reads occasionally in the literature of the commercial working of magnesium alloys the term "warm-working." This process, which in the case of rolling magnesium alloy involves metal heating to the temperature range 200°–300°C, is most often defined in terms of the favorable balance of strength and ductility that it yields. In structural terms, it generally takes advantage of recovery or partial recrystallization, either during the working process or during the cooling afterward. Thus, the equivalent of the two-stage step, cold-work plus annealing, is obtained.

The classical definitions used to separate recrystallization from the grain-growth step which follows it in an actual annealing treatment are that the grain boundaries move *away from* their centers of curvature in consumption of deformed grains during recrystallization, whereas they move *toward* their centers of curvature in the process of grain growth. However, it is not usually easy, even with careful metallographic study, to separate the two processes in sequence in the practical case of cold-rolled and annealed magnesium alloys. Two things of practical value to the metallurgist who is trying to control the properties of the wrought metal are the average grain size and the uniformity of grain size. A statement of the uniformity of sheet grain size is significant because rolled magnesium alloys tend to form "bands" of high-shear strain and fine recrystallized grain size. Three-dimensional plots of average grain size as a function of cold reduction in thickness by rolling and the temperature of annealing for 1 hr are presented for pure magnesium, a Mg-1.8% Mn alloy, and the commercial alloy AZ31B, which is nominally Mg-3% Al-1% Zn in Figs. 5.2-5.4.[5] The large grain sizes in Fig. 5.2 show a characteristic difficulty with grain-size control of unalloyed magnesium and are contributory to the low-strength capabilities of the wrought pure metal. On the other hand, AZ31B shows a consistently fine grain size with a variety of deformation and annealing conditions. As a result, it allows a rather wide flexibility of working conditions to be used to obtain maximum mechanical properties for commercial applications.

Fine grain size is obtainable in the Mg-1.8% Mn alloy if the large-grain germinating conditions of slight reduction and high annealing

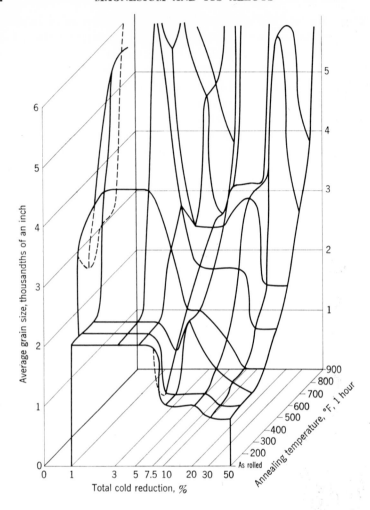

Fig. 5.2.  Recrystallization diagram for pure magnesium.[5]

temperature are avoided.  This behavior is probably associated with
the influence of twinning on recrystallization, as described below.

The specification of a "recrystallization temperature" for a given
magnesium alloy is occasionally found in the literature.  Such a parameter has little meaning unless it is accompanied by a rather complete history of the previous working conditions and the annealing
time.  The detection of recrystallized grains is clearly a question of

the resolution of such grains, which must have grown to a certain size to be detectable optically in a polished and etched section of the metal.

Some definitive work has been done to locate the sites of preferential recrystallization in both deformed polycrystalline aggregates and single crystals. In the case of polycrystalline magnesium alloys which have been deformed primarily in a compressive process such as simple compression, rolling, or forging, the compression bands, discussed in Section 4.2, are the sites of primary recrystallization. As recrystallization proceeds to completion, the volume of a lesser deformed matrix between the bands is consumed with the formation of new grains.

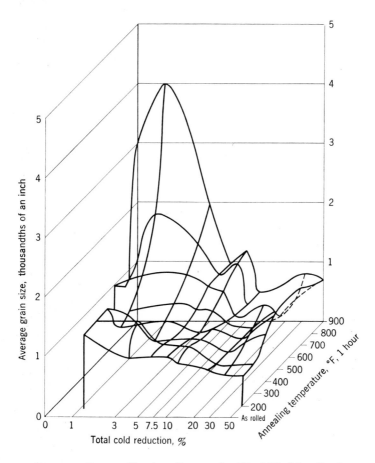

Fig. 5.3.  Recrystallization diagram for Mg-1.8% Mn alloy.[5]

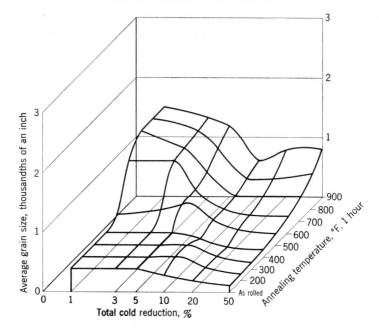

Fig. 5.4.   Recrystallization diagram for Mg-3% Al-1% Zn alloy.[5]

As may be seen in Fig. 4.7, the more highly deformed bands have recrystallized into grains of smaller size than those in the recrystallized volume between the bands.

The absence of any distinction between the preferred orientation of sheet and extrusions in the cold-worked and the hot-worked or recrystallized state in Section 4.5 is justified on the repeated observation that the (0002) pole figures of these materials show no pronounced change after recrystallization has occurred. However, for many years it was recognized that a rotation of grain orientation about the $c$ axis might be systematically involved in the recrystallization process. A study of the recrystallization of high-purity magnesium single crystal by Burke [6] has shown that the recrystallization texture and the deformation texture are related by polar rotations of approximately 30° about the $c$ axis in some grains. Other grains in his specimen did not rotate orientation at all in recrystallization.

The result of such reorientation in recrystallized magnesium alloy sheet might be apparent variable rotation about the $c$ axis. This effect has been observed in titanium by Sparks and Hammond.[7] They found that the basal pole figure was unchanged on recrystallization but the prismatic pole figure rotated 0° to 30°, depending on the annealing conditions. Barrett and Haller have presented evidence that, if a magnesium grain is twinned sufficiently, it will recrystallize in the twin orientation.[8]

Burke also found that $\{10\bar{1}2\}$ twin tips and intersections were the preferred sites for nucleation of the recrystallization. This is illustrated by the parallelism of the flat sides of the recrystallized grain to the residual $\{10\bar{1}2\}$ twins in Fig. 5.5.

Sturkey has compared recrystallized grain-size distributions in HK31 (Mg-3Th-1Zr) and AZ80 (Mg-8Al-0.5Zn) alloys.[9]  The results indicate that the main difference in the two alloys is much less secondary grain growth in HK31.  Nucleation rate in both materials followed an equation:

$$\dot{N} = \alpha t^4$$

where $t$ is time and $\alpha$ is a constant.  Nucleation was apparently uniform rather than random.

The mechanical properties of magnesium and its alloys are more dependent on grain size than those of the cubic structural metals, as

Fig. 5.5.  Magnesium crystal deformed 75% at room temperature and annealed 5 hr at 600°F.[6]  Flat sides of recrystallized grain parallel to residual twins, 150✕.

was pointed out in Chapter 4. Thus it is more important to have grain-size control in the manufacture of both cast and wrought magnesium alloy products. The principles and the difficulties involved are not markedly different from those encountered in the technology of cubic metals, however.

The rate of grain growth is dependent upon many variables. The ones of greatest importance appear to be temperature, initial grain size or shape, orientation (worked and recrystallized metal as compared with cast metal, for example), purity, and homogeneity of the metal. The purity influence is shown in a major way by the retarding effect on grain growth of massive second-phase particles which are not in solution in highly alloyed magnesium. A minor but often significant influence is that of very small, often microscopically irresolvable, particles of incidental impurities in otherwise pure magnesium or alloys which are solid solutions at the temperature of grain growth. In general, more problems with grain growth are experienced (1) the lower the alloying level; (2) the more of the second phase which is in solution at the elevated temperature; (3) the higher the temperature of the annealing or solution heat treatment; and (4) the more homogeneous the solid solution of the alloy.

The homogeneity factor is especially important in controlling the grain size in zinc- and aluminum-rich alloys. Germination in these alloys as well as grain growth in most magnesium alloy extrusions is far more dependent on solid-solution homogeneity than on the amount, shape, or distribution of second-phase particles. A practical application of this principle in the manufacture of magnesium alloy extrusions from powder is discussed in Section 7.7. An examination of the property grain-size plots in Chapter 4 shows that mechanical properties of magnesium are better the finer the grain size.

Magnesium alloy products are manufactured with good mechanical properties and satisfactory workability only by avoiding two other phenomena in addition to grain growth. The first is the recrystallization of extremely large grains at critical levels of deformation, particularly in the rolling process. The peak in Fig. 5.3 is such an example. This effect has been observed in the coiling of previously warm- or hot-rolled sheet. A small amount of $\{10\bar{1}2\}$ twinning on the compression side of the coiled sheet has caused the formation in recrystallization of excessively large grains which are cracking points in later working operations. The retention of an adequate amount of deformation to overcome this critical effect leads to satisfactory control of quality.[10, 11]

The second effect, that of the grain size in magnesium alloy castings, is controlled by many empirical methods of grain refinement. The details of grain-refining procedures are summarized in Chapter 6.

## 5.3  Precipitation

Magnesium alloys show generally three types of precipitation behavior. These are:

1. The rejection of an equilibrium solute-rich phase with little or no crystallographic coherency with the matrix solid solution. Age-hardening is negligible, although some dispersion-hardening may result from precipitate orientation. Examples of this group are Mg-Sn, Mg-Pb, and Mg-Mn binary alloys. Mg-Al binary alloys show this behavior in certain composition ranges and under certain conditions.

2. The formation of a nonequilibrium or transition precipitate which enjoys pronounced coherency with solid-solution matrix and which allows the development of true age-hardening. Later stages of the aging process involve the formation of an equilibrium solute-rich phase. The systems Mg-Zn, Mg-Li-Zn, Mg-Li-Al, and possibly Mg-Ce show this coherent precipitation.

3. The simultaneous recrystallization and precipitation of the equilibrium solute-rich phase at an advancing front throughout individual grains. This process was called "discontinuous precipitation" or the "recrystallization reaction" by Geisler.[12]  The terminology "cellular precipitation" was suggested by Turnbull.[13]  Mg-Al, Mg-Li-Zn, Mg-Li-Al, and commercial Mg-Al-Zn alloys are the known examples of this group among magnesium-based alloys.

**Magnesium-zinc alloys.** This system shows the most potent precipitation-hardening effects of any of the magnesium-based binary systems. Studies by Sturkey and Clark [14] of the alloys in the composition range 4–8% zinc have clarified the structure and orientation of the precipitates in this system. The authors found hardening by a general continuous precipitation, the particles of which are not clearly resolvable with the electron microscope until the alloys are overaged. Discontinuous precipitation at the grain boundaries is completely absent.

The early stages of the precipitation were most effectively studied with electron diffraction and single crystals of a 5% zinc alloy. The initial precipitate is not the equilibrium phase MgZn, but rather a transition phase MgZn'. The structure of this precipitate is the same as that of the Laves phase $MgZn_2$. Although the precipitate is not resolvable microscopically, the diffraction techniques show that it is present in arrays of rods which are perpendicular to the basal planes of the solid solution. The transition precipitate is extremely stable and even after aging 1000 hr at 500°F (260°C), coherency was not lost with the matrix. This coherency results from a close match of the $a$ parameter of the precipitate with the $c$ parameter of the solid solution. This rod orientation combined with the stable coherency provided an extremely effective block to basal slip and, thus, pronounced precipitation-hardening.

Although $d$ values have been published for the *equilibrium* zinc-rich phase, MgZn, its structure has not been determined completely.[15] It is clear that the transition phase and the equilibrium phase have different structures, although their relationship is not known at present. The conversion from one to the other is not studied easily because of the extreme stability of the former.

**Magnesium-cerium alloys.** Some investigations of precipitation in single crystals by Sturkey [9] indicate that the cerium-rich phase precipitates coherently, or at least epitaxially with the magnesium matrix. The lattice constants of the disordered phase are $a \cong c \cong 10.3$ A and the orientation relationship is:

$$a_{\text{Mg-Ce}} \parallel a_{\text{Mg}} \qquad c_{\text{Mg-Ce}} \parallel c_{\text{Mg}}$$

Any disorders occur parallel to the magnesium basal plane. As a consequence the *ordered regions* of the precipitate are rods perpendicular to this plane.

The work of Roberts on the creep behavior of these binary alloys shows that in the later stages of precipitation a preferred growth of precipitate particles at the grain boundaries occurs.[16] It is possible that the excellent creep resistance of alloys based on this binary system is controlled by this preferential precipitation at grain boundaries in addition to the coherent precipitate within the grains.

**Magnesium-tin and magnesium-lead alloys.** Precipitation of the equilibrium phase $Mg_2Sn$ as plates parallel to the (0001), $\{10\bar{1}1\}$, and $\{10\bar{1}2\}$ planes of the solid-solution matrix upon slow cooling from 560°C has been reported.[17] If aging is carried out at 250°C rather than by slow cooling, plates form parallel to the (0001) planes only. Three orientation relationships were found between the precipitate and matrix:

$$\{111\} \; Mg_2Sn \parallel (0001) \; Mg \qquad \text{and} \qquad \langle 110 \rangle \; Mg_2Sn \parallel \langle 10\bar{1}0 \rangle \; Mg$$

$$\{110\} \; Mg_2Sn \parallel (0001) \; Mg \qquad \text{and} \qquad \langle 110 \rangle \; Mg_2Sn \parallel \langle 10\bar{1}0 \rangle \; Mg$$

$$\{111\} \; Mg_2Sn \parallel (0001) \; Mg \qquad \text{and} \qquad \langle 110 \rangle \; Mg_2Sn \parallel \langle 11\bar{2}0 \rangle \; Mg$$

Later work showed the similarity between this system and the magnesium-lead alloy system,[18] as might be expected from the isomorphism of $Mg_2Sn$ and $Mg_2Pb$. When diffraction patterns are first observed, the precipitate platelets have the equilibrium structure. It is concluded that any coherency which may exist at the start of the process is lost very early. Negligible age-hardening results from a balance of the dispersion-hardening of the incoherent precipitate and the softening by matrix depletion.

**Magnesium-manganese alloys.** Sturkey has also investigated precipitation in this system.[9] The precipitate is cubic α-manganese which has the following orientation to the matrix:

$$\{111\} \text{ } \alpha\text{-Mn} \parallel (0002) \text{ Mg}$$

$$\{1\bar{1}0\} \text{ } \alpha\text{-Mn} \parallel \{10\bar{1}0\} \text{ Mg}$$

As a result of these orientation relations, two basic α-manganese orientations occur in a single magnesium grain and these are $\{112\}$ twins. Sturkey predicted that the precipitate would have the form of rods or ribbons parallel to $\langle 0002 \rangle$ directions in the magnesium and, thus, parallel to $\langle 111 \rangle$ directions in the α-manganese. His analysis was based on calculation of atomic mismatch between the two structures. The differences were large in all directions except $\langle 111 \rangle$ in the manganese, where it was only 1%. This prediction was confirmed by his electron diffraction patterns from a single crystal. This precipitate arrangement contributes some age-hardening capability to the binary system, although properties as outstanding as those of the magnesium-zinc alloys have never been realized.

**Magnesium-aluminum and magnesium-aluminum-zinc alloys.** Continuous and discontinuous precipitation are both observed in the Mg-Al alloys, and in the several commercial cast and wrought alloys that are based on the Mg-Al-Zn system. The ternary-based commercial-alloy group includes compositions up to 10% Al with Al-Zn ratios equal to or greater than 2:1. These alloys precipitate $Mg_{17}Al_{12}$, as do the Mg-Al binaries. When the Al-Zn ratio is near unity, ternary Mg-Al-Zn alloys do not show discontinuous precipitation.[19]

The continuous precipitation, which shows a Widmanstatten or crystallographically oriented structure in its overaged condition, is illustrated in Fig. 5.6. The discontinuous precipitation, which often starts at grain boundaries, is illustrated in Fig. 5.7. The work of several investigators [20-25] in both the binary and the ternary system leads to essential agreement on these points:

1. The discontinuous precipitation is predominant at lower aging temperatures but, above about 300°C, the continuous oriented precipitate is the major type.

2. The higher the temperature, the longer the time, and the lower the aluminum content, the coarser is the precipitate form and the greater the lamellar spacing in the discontinuous precipitate.

3. The finer the precipitate, and the less of the discontinuous precipitate, the higher are the room temperature tensile properties of the aged alloy.

4. The high-temperature continuous precipitate is oriented parallel to (0001) and the $\{11\bar{2}0\}$ planes of the solid-solution matrix.

5. There is no evidence that any sort of coherency or preprecipitation-hardening is occurring in the Mg-Al alloys. Strengthening effects are probably due to the dispersion of the equilibrium aluminum-rich phase and the essential grain refinement which the discontinuous precipitate may produce by virtue of the recrystallization associated with it.

6. The ratio of continuous precipitate to discontinuous precipitate is increased by the formation of $\{10\bar{1}2\}$ twins in the alloy before aging.

The only thorough study of the rate of Mg-Al alloy precipitation is that of Talbot and Norton.[20] They found that the Rockwell B hardness of a 9.6% Al alloy rose to a steady level in about 50 hr of aging at 150°C and 20 hr of aging at 175°C. No overaging effects were observed. The hardness maximum was reached when x-ray evidence showed less than 50% completion of the precipitation. Expansion curves obtained during aging correlated well with the percent precipitation curves obtained by x-ray diffraction.

Visible precipitation occurred in 0.5 hr at 175°C and 1.5 hr at 150°C, but was not present after 200 hr at 20°C and 100°C. Solution treatment was 24 hr at 415°C followed by a water quench. Talbot and Norton observed and photographed the discontinuous precipitation at the grain boundaries early in the aging. Later observations showed continuous precipitation within the grains.

The changes of many properties of sand-cast Mg-Al-Zn as a function of aging time at several temperatures have been measured by Leontis and Nelson.[25] Their curves show the sigmoidal shape characteristic of a nucleation and growth process. They correlated their results with dimensional growth during aging, a property change which reflects the progress of precipitation at least indirectly. Hardness and strength reached a maximum before growth was complete for AZ63A alloy (Mg-6Al-3Zn-0.2Mn) and at about the same time as completion of growth in AZ92A (Mg-9Al-2Zn-0.2Mn).

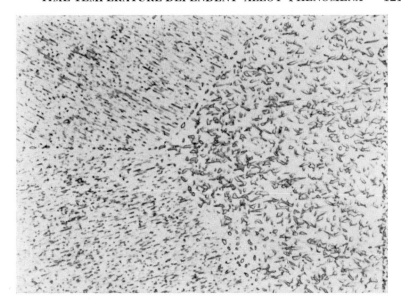

Fig. 5.6.  Continuous precipitation in Mg-8Al alloy, solution heat-treated and aged 8 hr at 500°F, 1000✕.  (Courtesty of J. B. Clark.)

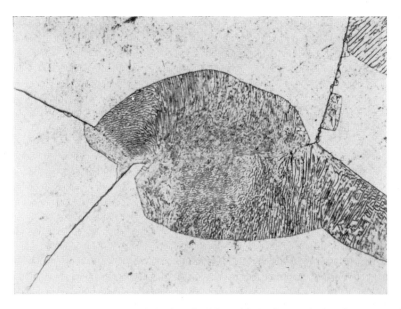

Fig. 5.7.  Discontinuous precipitation in Mg-8% Al alloy, solution heat-treated and aged 8 hr at 400°F, 500✕.  (Courtesy of J. B. Clark.)

Precipitation and strength changes occurred more rapidly at the same temperature in AZ92A than in AZ63A. The difference is more noticeable at higher aging temperatures. Leontis and Nelson showed the temperature dependence of the rate in their publication by a plot of the times to attain fixed percentages of maximum growth as the reciprocal of the absolute aging temperature. The plots are linear for temperatures below 450°F and correspond to "activation energies" of about $4 \times 10^4$ cal/g-atom. Leontis and Nelson did not carry the analysis to the point of reporting such a value. It may or may not have some relation to diffusion control in the precipitation process.

**Magnesium-lithium-zinc and magnesium-lithium-aluminum alloys.** Body-centered cubic lithium will contain about 90 weight % of magnesium in solid solution, allowing the preparation of magnesium-based alloys with this structure. The pronounced ductility of the cubic alloys has stimulated the study of systems that will, by a stable precipitation-hardening reaction, add strength to this ductility. Zinc and aluminum are two additions which proved to be useful in this respect.[26] Clark and Sturkey carried out a series of experiments on an alloy containing 50 atomic % lithium, 45 atomic % magnesium, and 5 atomic % zinc.[27] Aging temperatures ranged from 21°–150°C, and the kinetics and crystallography were studied by hardness measurements, metallography, and x-ray diffraction. They found the precipitation sequence to be:

$$\beta \xrightarrow{\quad} \text{MgLi}_2\text{Zn} \rightarrow \text{LiZn}$$

where $\beta$ is the cubic solid-solution matrix, $\text{MgLi}_2\text{Zn}$ is the coherent transition precipitate, and LiZn is the equilibrium second phase to which the transition structure reverts. The nonequilibrium transition structure is face-centered cubic B32 of the NaTl type with the lattice parameter of 6.64 A. The precipitation occurs with the following definite orientation relationship:

$$(100)_\beta \parallel (100) \text{ MgLi}_2\text{Zn} \parallel (100) \text{ LiZn}$$

$$[100]_\beta \parallel [100] \text{ MgLi}_2\text{Zn} \parallel [100] \text{ LiZn}$$

The habit plane of both the transition structure and the LiZn was found to be the cube plane of the matrix. Overaging at 200°F produces a Widmanstatten pattern which shows this habit clearly. Under certain aging conditions, discontinuous grain-boundary precipitate is observed in this system also. The hardness of this alloy reaches a maximum after aging 200 hr at 21°C. The calculated disregistry between the matrix solid solution and the transition precipitate structure is about 5%. Sturkey and Clark conclude that this large disregistry is the basic cause of the rapid age-hardening and the spontaneous overaging observed in these cubic alloys.

It has also been shown that, for alloys in the composition range where the equilibrium precipitate is MgLiZn rather than LiZn, the same transition structure $MgLi_2Zn$ forms.

Mg-Li-Al alloys in the equivalent composition range to the zinc-containing alloy just described exhibit the same precipitation behavior as that above. The equilibrium precipitate in this case is LiAl, and the transition precipitate, $MgLi_2Al$, has a lattice parameter of about 6.7 A. Observations of the age-hardening behavior of these aluminum-containing alloys show that the same arguments concerning stability of the precipitation process apply as in the case of the zinc-containing alloys.

**Magnesium-thorium alloys.** Because of the pronounced affinity of thorium for both hydrogen and oxygen, the age-hardening mechanism in actual alloys of this group is probably much more complicated than the solution and precipitation of Mg-Th phases. The addition of zirconium and/or manganese as in several commercially important alloys appears to complicate the precipitation process even more greatly. Sturkey has studied precipitation in HK31 (Mg-3Th-1Zr) and HM21 (Mg-2Th-1Mn-1Zr) alloys under conditions where hydride reactions are minimized.[9]

Aging in solution-treated HK31 precipitates both the equilibrium Mg-Th compound and a transition phase coherent with the Mg matrix. The equilibrium compound has a lattice parameter of 14.3–14.4 A and a probable composition $Mg_4Th$. The transition phase is cubic ($a_0 = 8.57$ A), and has the $Cu_2Mg$ or Laves-phase structure. Consequently its composition is probably $Mg_2Th$. A temperature rise affects the transformation rate of the transition phase less than it affects its rate of formation.

There is considerable disorder in the transition phase, parallel to one of the {111} planes, indicating that the growth of this (111) plane is parallel to the Mg basal plane ($d_{111} = 4.95$ A, $= c_{Mg}$ within 5%). This disorder is temperature-dependent, and more highly ordered particles may be obtained at higher temperatures.

Temperature changes have little effect on nucleation. The increase in precipitation rate due to cold-rolling results primarily from an increase in the number of nuclei. The quantitative x-ray spectrometer results from aged material may be described by the equation:

$$f = 1 - \exp - \left(\frac{t}{\tau}\right)^{\frac{1}{2}}$$

Where $f$ is the fraction of the thorium precipitated and $t$ is time. This relation applies in the range of $f$ from 0.3 to 0.9. Values of $\tau$ are:

| Temperature, °F | As Cast | 30% Cold-Rolled |
|---|---|---|
| 635 | 31 hr | 4.5 hr |
| 700 | 4.4 hr | 0.67 hr |

Since nucleation does not occur during aging, the "activation energy" for the process may represent that for the diffusion of thorium. It has been found to be 40–45 kcal/g-atom.

Precipitation in HM21 is much faster than in HK31. In the as-cast state, a temperature of 600°F for HM21 is about equivalent to 700°F for HK31. However, no transition phase has been found at any temperature of aging below 800°F. As with HK31, cold-work encourages precipitation. However, the shape of this precipitation curve suggests that nucleation occurs during the aging process. The precipitation of Mn and/or Th-Mn compounds apparently furnishes sufficiently energetic nuclei for the precipitation of Mg-Th without the necessity for the intermediate energy step of transition-phase precipitation.

## References

1. P. G. Shewmon and F. N. Rhines, "Rate of Self-Diffusion in Polycrystalline Magnesium," *Trans. AIME*, **200**, 1021 (1954).
2. P. G. Shewmon, "Self-Diffusion in Magnesium Single Crystals," *Trans. AIME*, **206**, 918 (1956).
3. G. A. Shirn, "Self-Diffusion in Thallium," *Acta Met.*, **3**, 87 (1955).
4. G. A. Shirn, "Self-Diffusion in Zinc," *Acta Met.*, **1**, 513 (1953).
5. H. A. Diehl (unpublished results), The Dow Chemical Company, Midland, Mich.
6. E. C. Burke (unpublished results), The Dow Chemical Company, Midland, Mich.
7. C. J. Sparks, Jr., and J. P. Hammond, "Preferred Orientations and Kinetics of Recrystallization in Titanium," *Wright Air Development Center Tech. Rept.*, No. 56-421 (July 1956).

8. C. S. Barrett and C. T. Haller, "Twinning in Polycrystalline Magnesium," *Trans. AIME,* **171**, 246 (1947).

9. L. Sturkey (unpublished results), The Dow Chemical Company, Midland, Mich.

10. E. C. Burke and C. Zvanut (patent application), The Dow Chemical Company, Midland, Mich.

11. H. Barbian, L. Britton, and G. Brackett (patent application), The Dow Chemical Company, Midland, Mich.

12. A. H. Geisler, in R. Smoluchowski, J. E. Mayer, and W. A. Weyl, *Phase Transformations in Solids,* John Wiley & Sons, New York, 1951, p. 387.

13. D. Turnbull, "Theory of Cellular Precipitation," *Acta Met.,* **3**, 55 (1955).

14. L. Sturkey and J. B. Clark (unpublished results), The Dow Chemical Company, Midland, Mich.

15. J. B. Clark and F. N. Rhines, "Central Region of the Mg-Zn Phase Diagram," *Trans. AIME,* **209**, 425 (1957).

16. C. S. Roberts, "Creep Behavior of Magnesium-Cerium Alloys," *Trans. AIME,* **200**, 634 (1954).

17. G. Derge, A. R. Kommel, and R. F. Mehl, "Studies Upon the Widmanstatten Structure. IX—The Mg-Mg$_2$Sn and Pb-Sb Systems," *Trans. AIME,* **124**, 367 (1937).

18. A. H. Geisler, C. S. Barrett, and R. F. Mehl, "Mechanism of Precipitation from Solid Solutions of Zinc in Aluminum, Magnesium in Aluminum and of Some Magnesium-Base Alloys," *Trans. AIME,* **152**, 201 (1943).

19. J. B. Clark (private communication), The Dow Chemical Company, Midland, Mich.

20. A. M. Talbot and J. T. Norton, "Age-Hardening of Magnesium-Aluminum Alloys," *Trans. AIME,* **122**, 301 (1936).

21. A Fisher, "A Note on Some Structural Changes Produced in a Magnesium Alloy by Heat-Treatment," *J. Inst. Metals,* **67**, 289 (1941).

22. W. Bulian and E. Fahrenhorst, "Über den Zerfall des Magnesium-Aluminum-Mischkristalls," *Z. Metallk.,* **34**, 285 (1942).

23. F. A. Fox and E. Lardner, "An Investigation of the Effects of Precipitation Treatment of Binary Magnesium-Aluminum Alloys," *J. Inst. Metals,* **49**, 373 (1943).

24. C. T. Haller and C. S. Barrett, "Precipitation in a Magnesium Sheet," *Trans. ASM,* **39**, 670 (1947).

25. T. E. Leontis and C. E. Nelson, "The Aging of Sand-Cast Mg-Al-Zn Alloys," *Trans. AIME,* **191**, 120 (1951).

26. R. S. Busk, D. L. Leman, and J. J. Casey, "The Properties of Some Magnesium-Lithium Alloys Containing Aluminum and Zinc," *Trans. AIME,* **188**, 945 (1950).

27. J. B. Clark and L. Sturkey, "The Age-Hardening Mechanism in Magnesium-Lithium-Zinc Alloys," *J. Inst. Metals,* **86**, 272 (1958).

# 6

# Casting Alloys
# and
# Technology

## 6.1 Introduction

The structural applications of magnesium were pioneered with castings. Long before the production of high-quality wrought products was brought under control, the foundrymen of Germany, England, the United States, and other countries had learned how to melt, alloy, and cast useful structures in magnesium. The statistics in Section 9.4 show that castings as a group still exceed the wrought products in tons shipped in the United States. The relative proportions are even higher in other countries.

Alloy and process development for casting magnesium has been directed toward the successful production of metal parts with the following desirable characteristics:

1. Adequate strength and ductility to compete with other light metal castings for a variety of normal-temperature applications.

2. The best possible mechanical properties for special high-temperature applications (up to and above the temperature of relatively rapid oxidation of magnesium in air, 400°C).

3. Minimum microporosity and freedom from hot-cracking to maintain strength and pressure tightness.

4. Freedom from flux contamination, with its attendant corrosion problems.

5. Satisfactory surface finish.

6. Wide variety of shapes and section sizes.

These characteristics have been obtained in alloy and process development in the following ways:

1. Judicious alloying has eliminated the columnar and coarse-grained characteristic of pure magnesium, yet with a minimum of difficulty with hot-cracking and microporosity.

2. Since the casting technology cannot take advantage of work-hardening to increase the strength of the structural part, as does the wrought-alloy technology, strength must be obtained by (a) solid-solution-hardening; (b) precipitation- or dispersion-hardening with second phases; and (c) grain refinement. All these are accomplished by proper alloying and heat treatment.

3. The discovery of a variety of special fluxes and the processes for using them has allowed the adequate protection of molten magnesium alloys from oxidation, the proper amount of refining action, and freedom from flux contamination in the casting.

4. Mold and core sands, risering, gating, and pouring techniques, permanent molds, and pressure die-casting molds especially suitable to magnesium alloys, with their low density, low specific heat, high thermal conductivity, and high oxidation tendency in the liquid state have been developed. Castings of large size and remarkable soundness are now made in large numbers.

The alloy designation system which has been standardized by the American Society for Testing Materials is used in referring to all alloys in this book. An essentially identical system has been adopted by the Canadian Standards Association. English producers of magnesium alloys have also found this system useful in competing in United States markets, and it seems possible that it may attain world-wide acceptance as a standard. It has the advantages of simplicity, flexibility, and adaptability to both cast and wrought products. *The use of the ASTM designation here does not necessarily imply that the composition under discussion has actually been submitted for adoption,* although this is usually true. In this system the first two letters indicate the principal alloying elements according to the following code:

A—aluminum
E—rare earth metals (elements 57–60 or combinations)
H—thorium
K—zirconium
L—lithium
M—manganese
Q—silver
T—tin
Z—zinc

The letter corresponding to the element present in the greater quantity in the alloy is given first. If they are equal in quantity, the letters are listed alphabetically. The two (or one) letters are followed by numbers which represent the *nominal* compositions in weight percent of the principal alloying elements. Information concerning third or fourth intentionally added elements, normal impurity levels, and exact specification contents of the principal elements are found in the complete chemical composition specification of the alloy itself. Suffix letters A,B,C, etc., refer to variations in composition within the nominal range. The suffix X indicates that the alloy is experimental and has not been finally adopted by the ASTM.

The heat-treated or work-hardened condition of the alloy (commercially referred to as its *temper*) is specified by a hyphenated suffix according to the following code:

| | |
|---|---|
| -F | as fabricated |
| -T4 | solution heat-treated |
| -T5, -T51 | artificially aged (without deliberate solution heat treatment) |
| -T6, -T61 | solution heat-treated and artificially aged |
| -T8 | solution heat-treated, worked, and artificially aged |
| -O | fully annealed |
| -H10, -H11 | slightly strain-hardened |
| -H23 | strain-hardened and partially annealed |
| -H24 | strain-hardened and partially annealed |
| -H26 | strain-hardened and partially annealed |

In general, the first four groups of designations are applicable to castings and the remainder to wrought magnesium alloy products. The entire scheme is presented here for reference in this chapter and for Chapter 7.

Magnesium casting alloys may be classified into groups with some degree of logic. The first group is based on the Mg-Al binary system and may be subdivided into those alloys containing zinc and manganese, respectively, as the second principal alloying element. The second group is based primarily on the Mg-Zn binary system and takes advantage of the grain-refining effect of zirconium additions. These two groups are primarily valuable for their structural behavior at normal or slightly elevated temperatures, say, less than 150°C. The third group is based on the magnesium–rare-earth-metal binary alloys. The fourth group is based on the Mg-Th binary system. The last two

Table 6.1.  Chemical Composition of Magnesium Casting Alloys

Chemical Composition, %

| ASTM Alloy | Al | Mn, Max. | Zn | Zr | Rare Earths | Th | Si, Max. | Cu, Max. | Ni, Max. | Other Imp. Max. |
|---|---|---|---|---|---|---|---|---|---|---|
| AM100A | 9.3–10.7 | 0.10 | 0.30 max. | — | — | — | 0.30 | 0.10 | 0.01 | 0.30 |
| AZ63A | 5.3–6.7 | 0.15 | 2.5–3.5 | — | — | — | 0.30 | 0.10 | 0.01 | 0.30 |
| AZ81A | 7.0–8.1 | 0.13 | 0.4–1.0 | — | — | — | 0.30 | 0.10 | 0.01 | 0.30 |
| AZ91A | 8.3–9.7 | 0.13 | 0.4–1.0 | — | — | — | 0.50 | 0.10 | 0.01 | 0.30 |
| AZ91B | 8.3–9.7 | 0.13 | 0.4–1.0 | — | — | — | 0.50 | 0.30 | 0.01 | 0.30 |
| AZ91C | 8.1–9.3 | 0.13 | 0.4–1.0 | — | — | — | 0.30 | 0.10 | 0.01 | 0.30 |
| AZ92A | 8.3–9.7 | 0.10 | 1.6–2.4 | — | — | — | 0.30 | 0.10 | 0.01 | 0.30 |
| EK30A | — | — | 0.3 max. | 0.20 min. | 2.5–4.4 | — | — | — | — | 0.30 |
| EK41A | — | — | 0.3 max. | 0.40–1.0 | 3.0–5.0 | — | — | — | — | 0.30 |
| EZ33A * | — | — | 2.0–3.5 | 0.50–1.0 | 2.5–4.0 | — | — | — | — | 0.30 |
| HK31A | — | — | — | 0.50–1.0 | — | 2.5–4.0 | — | — | — | 0.30 |
| HZ32A † | — | — | 1.7–2.5 | 0.05–1.0 | 0.10 | 2.5–4.0 | — | — | — | 0.30 |
| ZE41A ‡ | — | — | 3.5–5.0 | 0.40–1.0 | 0.75–1.75 | — | — | — | — | — |
| ZK51A § | — | — | 3.6–5.5 | 0.55–1.0 | — | — | — | — | — | 0.30 |
| ZH62A ‖ | — | — | 5.2–6.2 | 0.50–1.0 | — | 1.4–2.2 | — | — | — | 0.30 |

* British alloy ZRE1.
† British alloy ZT1.
‡ British alloy RZ5.
§ British alloy Z5Z.
‖ British alloy TZ6.

Table 6.2.    Room-Temperature Mechanical Properties
of Magnesium Casting Alloys

| Form | Alloy | Temper | TS, 1000 psi | | TYS,* 1000 psi | | Elongation in 2 in., % | |
|------|-------|--------|------|------|------|------|------|------|
| | | | Typ. | Min. | Typ. | Min. | Typ. | Min. |
| Sand casting | AZ63A | -F | 29 | 24 | 14 | 10 | 6 | 4 |
| and perma- | | -T4 | 40 | 34 | 14 | 10 | 12 | 7 |
| nent mold | | -T5 | 30 | 24 | 16 | 10 | 4 | 2 |
| casting | | -T6 | 40 | 34 | 19 | 16 | 5 | 3 |
| alloys | AZ81A | -T4 | 40 | 34 | 14 | 10 | 12 | 7 |
| | AZ91C | -F | 24 | 18 | 14 | 10 | 2 | — |
| | | -T4 | 40 | 34 | 14 | 10 | 11 | 7 |
| | | -T6 | 40 | 34 | 19 | 16 | 5 | 3 |
| | AZ92A | -F | 24 | 20 | 14 | 10 | 2 | 1 |
| | | -T4 | 40 | 34 | 14 | 10 | 10 | 6 |
| | | -T5 | 26 | 20 | 17 | 11 | 1 | — |
| | | -T6 | 40 | 34 | 21 | 18 | 2 | 1 |
| | EK30A | -T6 | 23 | 20 | 16 | 14 | 3 | 2 |
| | EK41A | -T5 | 23 | 20 | 16 | 14 | 1 | — |
| | | -T6 | 25 | 22 | 18 | 16 | 3 | 1 |
| | EZ33A | -T5 | 23 | 20 | 15 | 14 | 3 | 2 |
| | HK31A | -T6 | 30 | 27 | 15 | 13 | 8 | 4 |
| | HZ32A | -T5 | 29 | 27 | 14 | 13 | 7 | 4 |
| | ZE41A | -F | 26 | — | 15 | — | 5 | — |
| | | -T5 | 30 | 28 | 20 | 19 | 3.5 | 2.5 |
| | ZK51A | -F | 38 | — | 21 | — | 9 | — |
| | | -T5 | 40 | 34 | 24 | 20 | 8 | 5 |
| | ZH62A | -T5 | 40 | 35 | 25 | 22 | 6 | 4 |
| Permanent | AM100A | -F | 22 | 20 | 12 | 10 | 2 | — |
| mold casting | | -T4 | 40 | 34 | 13 | 10 | 10 | 6 |
| alloy | | -T6 | 40 | 34 | 16 | 15 | 4 | 2 |
| | | -T61 | 40 | 34 | 22 | 17 | 1 | — |
| Die-casting | AZ91A | -F | 33 | — | 22 | — | 3 | — |
| Alloy | AZ91B | | | | | | | |

* The compressive yield strength of cast magnesium alloys is essentially the
same as the tensile yield strength, hence is not shown.

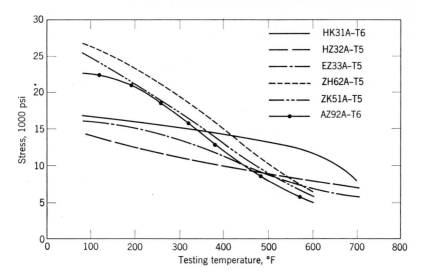

Fig. 6.1. Temperature dependence of tensile yield strength for sand-cast alloys. Separately cast test bars.[1,2]

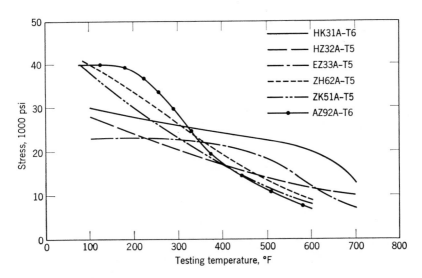

Fig. 6.2. Temperature dependence of tensile strength for sand-cast alloys. Separately cast test bars.[1,2]

groups are made up primarily of casting alloys which have been specifically designed for their elevated-temperature strength. Although
some of them may have outstanding normal-temperature properties,
they do not compete generally with alloys of the first two groups because of higher cost of the alloying elements. Table 6.1 summarizes
the compositions, and Table 6.2 presents the most important room-
temperature properties, of the casting alloys to be discussed in this
chapter.

The temperature dependence of the properties of many of them are
summarized in Figs. 6.1–6.4.[1, 2] The tensile yield strength in Fig. 6.1
is that derived from a 0.2% offset from the modulus line in the stress-
strain curve. The stresses in Fig. 6.4 are commercially useful parameters that represent complete creep curves by one value of both strain
and time. These data were obtained from separately cast test bars.
Such test bars are more representative of sections of actual castings

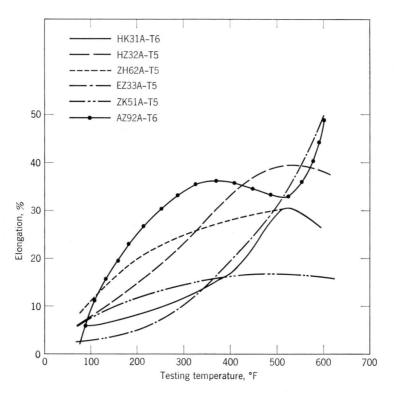

Fig. 6.3. Temperature dependence of tensile ductility for sand-cast alloys.
Separately cast test bars.[1, 2]

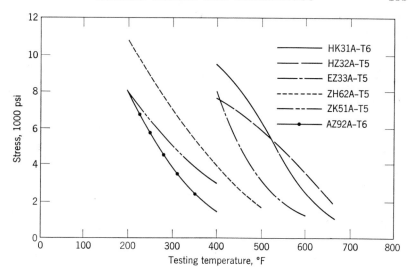

Fig. 6.4. Temperature dependence of creep limit for 0.2.% total extension in 100 hr for sand-cast alloys. Separately cast test bars.[1,2]

than are most other casting metals.  Little or no change in mechanical properties is observed when the skin is machined from a magnesium alloy casting.

Current sales literature in the industry presents a more complete statement of some properties, such as fatigue resistance, bearing strength, hardness, shear strength, and relative corrosion resistance, than space allows here.[3,4]  However, the most important mechanical properties are tensile yield strength (0.2% offset from the modulus line), (ultimate) tensile strength, compressive yield strength, and percent tensile elongation in 2 in.  The variation of these properties with temperature of test, and the creep properties as a function of temperature, are treated here in a fairly complete manner.  These properties show the comparative position of the alloys with respect to each other in the technology of today and also demonstrate the position the magnesium casting alloys as a group hold with respect to other presently castable materials.

## 6.2  Magnesium-Aluminum-Based Casting Alloys

In the United States the sand-casting alloys AZ63A and AZ92A have been the principal materials for normal-temperature applications for many years.  Until the advent of the use of zirconium as a potent grain refiner, they were essentially the only alloys that froze with an adequately fine grain to give mechanical properties that would attract the designer to use magnesium at all.  They offer a satisfactory combination of strength and ductility.  They are castable with no difficulty from hot-cracking or tearing.  The tendency to show microporosity, more pronounced in AZ63A, is minimized in good foundry technique by the avoidance of thin horizontal sections and the use of large feeder volumes as much as possible.  Both of these alloys are benefited greatly by heat treatment, and it is standard practice to treat them. Common solution heat-treatment conditions are 10 hr at 388°C (730°F) for AZ63A and 20 hr at 405°C (760°F) for AZ92A.  A typical precipitation-aging treatment for both alloys is 5 hr at 215°C (420°F).  A protective atmosphere of a few tenths of a percent of sulfur dioxide in air is recommended for the solution heat treatment to minimize oxidation of the casting.  Rather close control of the solution heat-treatment temperature is important, since heating above the solidus, which is about 445°C for these alloys, will lead to some grain boundary melting and to void formation which drastically lower mechanical properties of any overheated age-hardenable alloy.  Slow heating to the final temperature is also important to remove low-melting, nonequilibrium constituents.  The -T5 temper is typically accomplished by aging 4 hr at 260°C (500°F) for either alloy.  It has been principally used to carry the precipitation process to such a point that slightly elevated temperature service of the casting will not lead to the growth which is characteristic of aging in these alloys.[5]  The mechanical properties are at the same time lower than for the -T6 temper.

The AZ91 alloys are especially suitable for die casting but also offer high tensile yield strength in sand and permanent mold castings.  Both yield strength and ductility are good, and the castings produced from this group are pressure-tight.  The composition AZ81A, although of rather low yield strength, offers high ductility for designs where both ductility and the economy of the Mg-Al-based alloys are desired.

Although there has been a pronounced trend away from the simple compositions of magnesium casting alloys, AM100A, which is essentially a Mg-Al binary with the minimal amount of manganese addition, has remained as a popular alloy for obtaining high tensile yield and elongation in castings which can be made by the permanent mold process.

## 6.3  The Addition of Zirconium to Magnesium Alloys

To understand the development of all the remainder of the casting alloys in Tables 6.1 and 6.2, as well as of many of the wrought alloys in Chapter 7, the importance of the grain-refining effect of zirconium additions is appropriately discussed at this point. Although there may be some uncertainties on the historical details because of the occurrence of World War II at a key time in the development of zirconium-containing alloys, the earliest work on the subject is traceable to the research group of the German I. G. Farbenindustrie plant in Bitterfeld and in particular to F. Sauerwald. In a comprehensive review article on the subject of the Mg-Zr and the Mg-Th-Zr alloys,[6] Sauerwald himself sets 1937 as the year when the profound grain-refining effects of zirconium were first discovered. His bibliography indicates the intensive effort that continued through the war years, although the results of such efforts were obtainable for the most part only in patents and internal reports written during the period. Publication of the results in the open literature after the war occurred in profusion under Sauerwald's name. In one postwar paper he cited 0.6% as the critical zirconium content.[7] At a later date, workers in the United States and England cited higher and wider ranges of zirconium content, as Table 6.1 shows. *This small amount of zirconium completely eliminated the columnar and coarse-grained cast structure which was found up to that time in all except the aluminum-containing alloys.* Satisfactory mechanical properties in cast magnesium alloys can only be obtained with a fine-grained structure. The variety of alloy systems that could be considered as the base for magnesium casting alloys was immediately increased greatly.

There were many problems in the development of a practical alloying procedure, however. Elemental zirconium is not an efficient agent to use because of its high melting point, high oxidation tendency, and high cost. The effort was focused in the early German work on the use of reducible zirconium salts which could be stirred into the melt as an alloying flux. This approach has been used with variations to the present day. According to Ball, the Bitterfeld group found the problem of alloying in this manner so difficult that they eventually abandoned their effort on the alloying-process development in about 1942.[8] However, work continued on the problem at Magnesium Elektron Ltd. in England, and, shortly after the war, The Dow Chemical Company in the United States increased effort on the program started before the war on zirconium-containing alloys and on methods of producing them. The major problem was the avoidance of corrosive flux inclusions when zirconium salts were used.[9] A second problem was the elimination of the microporosity that was continually associated with the cast structure of some of the more attractive alloys. The large number of commercial zirconium-containing alloys in Tables 6.1 and 6.2 is evidence that these problems have been brought under control. The British process depends on the use of fluoride-chloride mixtures in the flux, whereas the American practice is based on the use of Mg-Zr master alloys which have been produced from the reduction of zirconium chloride by the melt.[10]

Paradoxically enough, the addition of zirconium is incompatible with the alloying elements aluminum and manganese, the important components of alloys that may be effectively grain-refined by other methods. Both of these elements are precipitated from the liquid solution when zirconium is present.[11] No such disabling interaction occurs in the case of alloys containing zinc, rare earth metal, or thorium. Since one of the functions of manganese in the Mg-Al-based alloys—to assist in the maintenance of a low iron content in the melt at pouring time—is satisfactorily performed by zirconium itself, manganese can be conveniently eliminated from the zirconium-containing alloys, as shown in Table 6.1. The mechanism by which zirconium grain-refines magnesium is not at all clear, although some suggestions have been made that, with the peritectic equilibrium occurring in the binary system (see Fig. 3.27), zirconium-rich particles are produced early in the freezing of the alloys and magnesium grains are profusely nucleated upon them.[7] This nucleation is thought to result from the near identity of interatomic distances in the hexagonal close-packed structures of both elements. Indeed, the pronounced zirconium-rich coring that has been observed in cast ZK51A supports this view.

### 6.4  Magnesium-Zinc-Based Casting Alloys

The highest combinations of tensile yield strength and elongation at room temperature in magnesium casting alloys occur in the two high-zinc-content alloys ZK51A-T5 and ZH62A-T5. Alloys with such high zinc contents were not castable in fine grain size until the technology of zirconium addition was developed.[12] The extremely potent precipitation-hardening of the Mg-Zn binary system combined with the grain-refining effect of the Zr binary system allows the attainment of high strengths in these alloys. However, as the zinc content is increased, in general more problems are encountered with micro-porosity and hot-cracking in the casting. These problems are associated with the low solidus and the pronounced segregation in the Mg-Zn system. In the case of ZK51A, careful foundry technique, in particular the avoidance of large horizontal thin sections in the casting design, allows castings of satisfactory soundness to be made.[13] The thorium in ZH62XA helps to reduce these problems even further. The use of a rare-earth-metal addition in ZE41A-T5 also allows the production of sound castings with considerable certainty, although the mechanical properties are not quite as high as with the other two high-zinc-containing alloys.

The strength of the magnesium-high zinc alloys decreases from the high room-temperature levels rather rapidly with increasing temperature, Figs. 6.1 and 6.2. The creep resistance of these alloys is better than that of the typical Mg-Al-based casting alloy AZ92A. However, even though ZH62A contains a moderate amount of thorium, it cannot be considered a leading high-temperature alloy. This group is outstanding for its toughness and strength below 150°C (300°F), when properly cast and heat-treated. A typical heat treatment for ZK51A is 12 hr at 177°C (350°F). Heat treatment of 2 hr at 350°C (625°F), followed by 16 hr at 180°C (355°F), is normal for both ZE41A and ZH62A. A single aging of 24 hr at 250°C (480°F) is an alternative which does not give quite as good stress relief.

### 6.5    Magnesium–Rare-Earth-Metal–Based Casting Alloys

Although the Mg-Al- and Mg-Zn-based casting alloys may often be considered for service temperatures up to 150°C (300°F) or greater, depending upon service requirements, needs have arisen in modern technology for light alloys that will operate at much higher temperatures. The creep behavior of these alloys is especially important. To minimize creep strain, effective blocking of strain within the grains and especially at grain boundaries by precipitates which are stable at high temperatures is desirable. A high recrystallization temperature is also desirable to minimize creep strain by recrystallization softening. The Mg-Al-based alloys are poor in both respects. The discontinuous precipitation phenomenon offers no strengthening of grain boundaries but rather a multiplication of them.[14] The bulk recrystallization temperature is relatively low in these alloys also.

The magnesium–rare-earth-metal–based group has outstanding creep as well as short-time tensile properties in the temperature range 150–

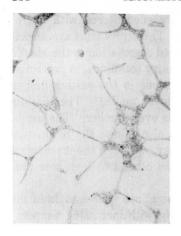

Fig. 6.5.   Microstructure of as-cast EK30 alloy,[20] 500X.

260°C (300–500°F).   All of them depend upon zirconium additions for grain refinement.   The outstanding alloy in this group at present is EZ33A.   Some of its high-temperature properties are summarized in Figs. 6.1 to 6.4.   As an alloy it occupies a position between the high-zinc- and high-aluminum-containing alloys, on the low side, and the thorium-containing alloys, on the high side.   The differences between the alloying effects of different combinations of rare earth metals in the magnesium alloys have been studied.[15,16]   In general, it appears that, as the principal alloying element is moved in the direction of increasing atomic number, i.e., from lanthanum to praseodymium, the

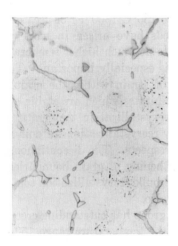

Fig. 6.6.   Microstructure of heat-treated and aged EK30 alloy,[20] 500X.

creep resistance is increased. However, the differences within the series are secondary compared to the advantages shown by the group as a whole when compared with the Mg-Al- and Mg-Zn-based alloys. Therefore, for commercial alloys, mischmetal (50% cerium; remainder, other rare earth metals), which is less costly than the more completely separated rare earth metals, is generally used.

The importance of precipitation-hardening in the elevated-temperature strength of these alloys is shown by the small benefit in greatly exceeding the maximum solid solubility of the rare earths.[15,17,18] The particular mechanism of this creep resistance has been found from a study of Mg-Ce alloys.[19] Cerium precipitates profusely and preferentially at grain boundaries in magnesium during the aging treatment. These localized particles of the cerium-rich intermetallic phase are very effective blocks to the operation of the grain boundary migration which is normal in pure magnesium or in the Mg-Al alloys at elevated temperatures and low strain rates. The precipitation of cerium occurs also throughout the grains.

The rare earth metal alloys give no difficulty from microporosity or hot-cracking. This fortunate behavior probably results from the short solidification range, even though the segregation is as high as in the Mg-Zn-based alloys. Some foundry difficulties are encountered with an increased oxidation tendency in the alloys because of the stability of all the rare earth metal oxides.

The corrosion resistance of EK30A or EK41A, with no zinc content, is reportedly the best of the group.[20] The corrosion resistance of this group of alloys is good when compared to that of the Mg-Al-based alloys. Solution heat treatment is commonly performed for 18 hr at a maximum temperature of 570°C (1060°F). Artificial aging is carried out in 16 hr at 205°C (400°F). The higher solution heat-treatment temperature and the highly sloped solidus make the temperature control and necessity for protective atmosphere even more critical than in the case of heat-treating AZ63A and AZ92A.

The characteristic microstructures of as-cast and heat-treated magnesium–rare-earth-metal–based alloys are presented in Figs. 6.5 and 6.6. The eutectic may show various degrees of divorcement, and the precipitate may show different levels of resolution.

## 6.6   Magnesium-Thorium-Based Casting Alloys

Another of the discoveries of Sauerwald, while working in the Bitterfeld group, was that thorium was a powerful alloying element for con-

Fig. 6.7.   Microstructure of HZ32A-T5 alloy,[23] 500×.

ferring creep resistance on magnesium. The initial discovery seems to date to before 1940, but work on this alloy group was hampered in all countries by the war effort. After the war, both Magnesium Elektron Ltd. in England and The Dow Chemical Company in the United States began development of commercial magnesium alloys in earnest. The two casting alloys that emerged with outstanding creep resistance in the temperature range 200–300°C (390–660°F), HZ32A and HK31A, differ somewhat in rank across the range, as is evident in Figs. 6.1, 6.2, and 6.4. At very short times or in the lower end of the temperature range, HK31A is superior, whereas, at the higher temperatures and low strain rate applications, HZ32A has more load-carrying capacity.[21–24]

This group of alloys depends greatly on the grain-refining effects of zirconium to counteract what would normally be a columnar cast structure.[25,26] The thorium-containing alloys cast with no microporosity or hot-cracking problems. However, they are even more susceptible than the rare-earth-metal–containing alloys to oxidation before pouring. HK31A is normally used in the -T6 temper, produced by a 2-hr solution heat treatment at 565°C (1050°F) and a 16-hr aging at 205°C (400°F). HZ32A is commonly used in the -T5 temper produced by a 16-hr aging at 315°C (600°F).

The addition of rare earth metals to any of the Mg-Th-based alloys generally decreases creep resistance. The microstructure of the Mg-Th-based alloys is not greatly different from that of the magnesium–

rare-earth-metal–based alloys. A peculiar combination of acicular and jagged microstructure has been observed in HZ32A-T5, Fig. 6.7. This structure is associated with high creep resistance, according to Nelson.[23]

## 6.7   The Melting of Magnesium Alloys

Steel containers are almost universally used to melt down, transfer, and hold molten magnesium. The small solubility of iron in the liquid and the known methods for precipitating it rather completely before the metal is poured allow this convenient use of iron alloys. A maximum nickel content of 0.2% is allowed in these alloys. In some cases the outside of the larger pots is given an aluminum coating, but, at present, there is no certainty that the increased life of the container is worth the cost of the aluminizing. Melt poisoning may result from use of aluminized pots with zirconium-containing alloys.

The nature and the rate of the oxidation of molten magnesium are such that surface protection is always required for the melt. The compositions of five fluxes used in contemporary American practice are listed in Table 6.3. These compositions, developed by The Dow Chemical Company, fall roughly into three categories. The high-fluidity refining fluxes, types 220 and 230, are stirred into the melt and form

**Table 6.3.   Flux Compositions Developed by The Dow Chemical Company and Used Widely in American Magnesium Foundry Practice**

Weight %

| Dow No. | KCl | MgCl$_2$ | BaCl$_2$ | CaCl$_2$ | CaF$_2$ | MgO | MnCl$_2$ |
|---|---|---|---|---|---|---|---|
| 230 | 55 | 34 | 9 | | 2 | | |
| 310 | 20 | 50 | | | 15 | 15 | |
| 311 | 30.5 | 29 | 8.5 | | 10.5 | 11.5 | |
| 220 | 57 | | 12.5 | 28 | 2.5 | | |
| 250 | 23 | | 2.5 | | 2.5 | | 72 |
| 320 | | | | | 13 | 11 | 76 |
| 232 | 37.5 | 42 | 4.5 | | 8.5 | 7.5 | |
| 234 | 25 | 50 | 20 | | 5 | | |

a liquid layer on the surface of the melt which does not change characteristics with holding time. They are most suitable to the foundry operation of the *open-pot* variety, where hundreds of pounds of molten metal are alloyed and held in reserve for transfer to a pressure die-casting machine or to smaller containers for the pouring of sand or permanent mold castings.[27] The inspissated flux, type 310, forms with time a semisolid crust over the surface of the melt, which can be more easily held back during a final pouring operation, thus leading to far less risk of flux contamination in the casting than with the high-fluidity fluxes.[28] This flux is most suited to the foundry operations of the *crucible* type, where the melting is done in the crucible from which the casting is to be poured.[27] Most large-scale magnesium foundry operations in the United States employ the open-pot type of flux at the pre-melting, alloying, and holding stages, and the crucible type of flux in the final superheating and pouring stages. Type 250 and 320 fluxes are used to increase and control the manganese content of the alloy in the open-pot and the crucible operations respectively.

The 220, 232, and 234 fluxes are used in the cold-chamber pressure die-casting process. They are mainly refining fluxes in this application and they offer very little surface protection. The prevention of oxidation in this process is mainly by the use of a sulfur dioxide baffle system. Small amounts of sulfur, sulfur dioxide, and other special agents are also used to protect the exposed surfaces of the melt and the stream when the final crucible flux crust is pulled back in the pouring of sand castings.

The 230 and 310 fluxes are well adapted to the protection of the Mg-Al-based casting alloys, which still make up the bulk of the world's foundry output. They both contain large amounts of $MgCl_2$. However, alloys which contain appreciable quantities of rare earth metals or thorium, as do most of the newly developed magnesium alloys, are best melted under a flux which is low in $MgCl_2$. The most suitable flux for these alloys is type 311. Because of the pronounced tendency for preferential oxidation of the rare earth metals or the thorium, it is more essential to ensure the use of an adequate amount of flux than in the case of the Mg-Al-based alloys, where 2–4% flux consumption is normal.

A chlorination step has been added to many foundry operations as an effective and convenient substitute for the stirring in of a refining flux. Chlorination has the double advantage of reducing oxides in the melt and also of reducing the amount of dissolved gases, in particular hydrogen, which may lead to microporosity in the casting.[29–32] Either chlorination or flux refining is generally carried out in the temperature range 715–760°C (1320–1400°F). The chlorine is often introduced through a graphite tube and is allowed to bubble through the melt for 5–15 minutes as rapidly as will avoid splashing. The upper melt temperature is fixed by the rate of excessive formation of $MgCl_2$.

Fluxing and melting practices in England differ in detail from those outlined here. In particular, the use of separate high-fluidity and inspissated fluxes and the use of chlorination appear to be not so common. However, the main principles of the melting operation—to protect the melt from oxidation, to refine it, and to adjust its composition with regard to major alloying elements as well as to minor impurities, such as iron—must be the same as in the United States.

Gas flames under the pots are the most common heat sources for magnesium alloy melting operations in the foundry. However, electric-resistance-heated pots and transfer furnaces have been used with success. Low-frequency-induction melting has also been used. Considerable experimentation has been carried out with the direct-flame or reverberatory melting of magnesium at the Dow laboratories.[27] Both oil and gas were used as a fuel. The method offers advantages of safety and fuel economy over conventional melting methods. However, its lack of suitability for fine scrap and its lesser freedom of surface protection control have prevented widespread application.

There are certain precautions that must be observed in the safe and successful melting of magnesium. As in the melting practice of all metals, the introduction of water into the melt is *disastrous*. The hygroscopic nature of $MgCl_2$, which is a principal flux ingredient, adds to the necessity of care in the drying of all tools (skimmers, ladles, etc.) which are to be introduced into the melt. Often separate pots of molten type 230 flux are maintained for the periodic washing of all tools. All solid metal which is to be melted must be cleaned of oil and moisture before charging.

The wall thicknesses of all containers of molten metal must be checked periodically, and crucibles must be taken out of service when their walls become so thin as to be dangerous. The gas-fired settings under open pots are kept free of the accumulation of any iron oxide scale, which undergoes a violent thermit reaction with molten magnesium in the case of a pot leak. The stirring into the melt of refining fluxes leads to a gradual buildup of sludge in the bottom of the melting pots and crucibles. This deposit must be held to a minimum by constant removal to maintain both cast-metal quality and safe operation.

## 6.8   Grain Refinement

Fine-grained castings of magnesium alloys are produced by: (1) superheating the melt to 900–925°C (1650–1700°F) for a few minutes, then cooling to the casting temperature, 730–870°C (1350–1600°F); (2) the addition of carbon in the form of lamp black, hydrocarbons, or other organic compounds at 760–788°C (1400–1450°F); or (3) the inclusion of 0.6–0.8% zirconium in the alloy.   As can be seen in Table 6.1, all except the Mg-Al-based alloys contain zirconium. Thus only this latter group is subjected to the superheating or carbon-addition treatments.   The two treatments are not used together because grain coarsening often results from the combination.

Although the mechanism of grain refinement is not completely understood, Sturkey and Joseph have presented a plausible hypothesis based on changes in the Mn-Al compounds which are present in the Mg-Al-based alloys.[33]   They hypothesize a continual breakup of $MnAl_6$ into many small fragments of lower aluminum content in accordance with the Mn-Al phase diagram, as the melt is superheated. During cooling, these small particles of $MnAl_4$, or perhaps $MnAl_3$, deplete the melt near them of aluminum.   Thus a high density of shells which freeze at a higher temperature than the equilibrium liquidus is established.   These shells serve as nuclei for the remainder of the melt. Certain predictions have been made on the basis of this hypothesis. The known experimental results are in general agreement with these predictions, although further test of this mechanism would be desirable.   Sturkey and Joseph also found that about 0.002% beryllium or zirconium and about 0.08% thorium will each prevent grain refinement by superheating.   Copper in amounts up to 0.5% does not prevent superheating refinement.   Although the primary mechanism is thought to depend on the presence of manganese in the alloy, 0.1% calcium will refine the grain at 760°C (1400°F), even though manganese is practically absent.

Burns[34] and Mann[35] also observed the grain-coarsening effect of small amounts of beryllium.   Beryllium also markedly inhibits burning of magnesium to the degree that it may be held molten without fluxes.

## 6.9   The Sand Casting of Magnesium Alloys

Molds are made from synthetic sands of rather closely controlled fineness in the range of 60 to 80 on the American Foundrymen's Society scale. This range, which is considerably coarser than that used for the casting of other metals, is chosen to allow a maximum of permeability in the mold, a factor of prime importance in the successful casting of magnesium alloys. Elliott gives two reasons for high-permeability sand: [36]

1. The low specific gravity of magnesium allows gases generated in the mold material to be forced into the liquid metal, unless such gases can escape freely by traveling through the mold material into the venting system of the mold.
2. The passage of mold gases through the walls of a magnesium casting while they are still liquid results in casting defects.

Bentonite clay and water are used as the binder for the green sand in the mold. Other minor binder additions, such as wood flour or cereal, may be used for special purposes. An important addition to the molding mix for magnesium foundry operations are inhibitors, which control the marked tendency of liquid magnesium to reduce the water, sand, or clay. Boric acid, sulfur, glycols, and nonvolatile fluorides are used successfully as inhibitors. A typical mix contains 2–4% bentonite and 4–5% inhibitors. Fairly careful control of the molding-sand temperature is used in the better foundries to minimize variations in the working characteristics of the sand in the molding step.

Cast magnesium alloy flasks are in widespread use in American magnesium foundries. Their light weight, rigidity, and accuracy make them highly satisfactory for the production of large or small sand castings. The mechanical aspects of mold making in the magnesium foundry are much the same as for other metals. Mechanical equipment of advanced type is adaptable to the operations. Careful gauging of molds and cores leads to higher quality and more consistent casting production. Magnesium alloy gauges have found an especially good application here.

The making of cores for sand-casting magnesium is one of the most important parts of the operation. Ideally, it is desired that the core sand mix have high green strength to allow dimensional accuracy, high flowability to allow mechanical operations, high baked strengths to allow normal handling, and high collapsibility to allow rapid breakdown despite the low specific heat of the solidifying magnesium. The best compromise of these needs is obtained with the use of the synthetic binder urea formaldehyde in fairly coarse sand in conjunction with natural bentonite binder. A typical formula for a core sand mix is as follows: [37]

| | |
|---|---|
| Silica (65 mesh) | |
| Bentonite | 5% |
| Urea formaldehyde | 2–4% |
| Cereal | 1% |
| Ammonium silicofluoride | 1.25–2.25% |
| Sulfur | 1–1.25% |
| Boric acid | 1–1.25% |
| Dipropylene glycol | 0.2% |
| Water | 3% |

When urea formaldehyde is used in this manner, the core is properly baked in about 20 minutes at 160°C (320°F). With these recent improvements in the technology of core making for the magnesium foundry, mold design is moving in the direction of a more extensive use of cores.

Mold designs for high-quality complex castings of magnesium alloys are unique in the foundry field. The gating and risering is more elaborate than for the casting of other metals.[38] The low density and the low specific heat of the metal require larger heads of molten metal

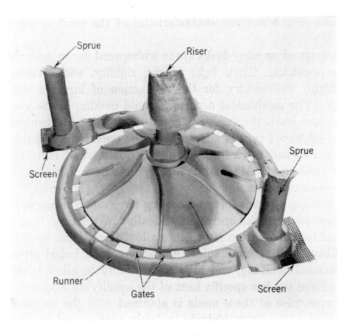

Fig. 6.8. High-symmetry magnesium alloy casting after shakeout showing the simplest elements of sand casting. (Courtesy of K. E. Nelson.)

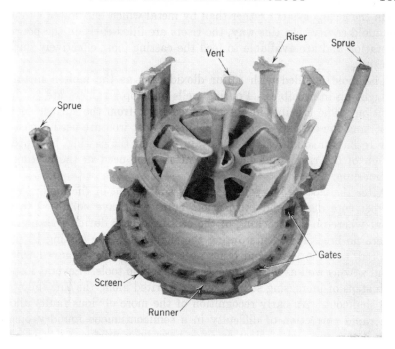

Fig. 6.9. Magnesium alloy cast wheel after shakeout. (Courtesy of K. E. Nelson.)

and shorter distances of travel during the freezing process. The oxidation tendency of the liquid metal prohibits the use of top pouring. If the metal is fed into the casting from the top, oxides are entrapped in it. A typical mold design is demonstrated by the castings in Figs. 6.8 and 6.9. The molten magnesium is brought to the lowermost level of the casting through down-sprues which are either located as centrally as possible in the casting or symmetrically about the periphery, as shown in the photographs. At this point it is passed through an arrangement of screens made from perforated sheet steel. The screens serve two purposes—the entrapment of particles of oxide of flux which are thus prevented from entering the casting, and the minimization of turbulence in the incoming metal flow. Equivalent filters are also often used at the top of the pouring well. After filtration, the metal is distributed through a complex of runners and gates, with the object of reducing the distance through which any volume of metal must move before filling the mold cavity. Large risers are used in abundance to maintain the mold filling head. Often risers are filled directly from the gating system rather than by metal which has flowed through the mold cavity. In this way, the risers are filled early in the pouring operation and are available to feed the casting most effectively during freezing.

The mold is filled with sulfur dioxide gas as the molten metal is brought up in crucibles. Pouring wells and top strainers are set into position. The crucible flux is skimmed back from the surface of the melt, and the casting is poured. Chills of cast iron are used occasionally to hasten solidification in certain parts of the casting, but careful design of the risers and gates minimizes their need in the casting of magnesium.

After the casting has solidified, it is shaken out of the mold. With correct core design and fabrication, cores will have collapsed to the point where no hot-cracking of the casting occurs during freezing and where no breakage occurs during the shakeout. The casting is sand-blasted, and the risers and other accessory parts are removed with a band saw as well as with conventional machine tools. Several inspection steps of increasing stringency are merited along the line following the shakeout. An early recognition of the more obvious faults allows the rapid correction of difficulty in a semicontinuous foundry operation before too many reject castings have been produced.

Final steps of the treatment of the magnesium casting may involve radiographic inspection, heat treatment, straightening, repair welding, impregnation for pressure tightness, chemical coating, and special machining.

Elliott has made an interesting summary of the metal economy of the founding of magnesium alloys.[36] He quotes the average ratio of poured metal to castings shipped in a present-day quality magnesium foundry as 4:1. Since it is necessary to leave a substantial amount of metal in the bottom of the pouring crucible in order to avoid flux contamination, as much as 6 lb of metal must be melted for every pound of castings finally shipped. The magnitude of these ratios is simply a reflection of the abundant and complicated use of risers and gates described above. These parts are returned for remelting, of course, but, in their removal, a quantity of fines are produced which are recovered only partially. Chlorination and oxidation remove magnesium metal from the systems. The combination of all loss factors requires that, for every 100 lb of castings sold, 120 to 125 lb of raw metal must be added to the metal system in a quality foundry.

As has been discussed above, certain elements in magnesium alloys are incompatible for various reasons. The versatile magnesium foundry may be remelting Mg-Al-, Mg-Zn-, Mg–rare-earth-metal– and Mg-Th-based alloy scrap. A useful spot test has been found by Nelson and Strieter to separate rare-earth-containing alloys and those containing aluminum and/or zinc.[20] A clean metal surface is prepared by grinding, sanding, or sawing. A drop of dilute HCl is placed on the surface followed by a drop of 3% $H_2O_2$ after a few seconds. Rare earth metal in the alloy will cause a yellowish foam. Aluminum and/or zinc will cause a gray-to-black precipitate. No precipitate is obtained from commercially pure magnesium or KO alloy.

## 6.10   The Permanent Mold and Pressure Die Casting of Magnesium Alloys

The permanent mold casting process is essentially a variant of the sand casting process. Gravity is depended upon to feed the mold cavity, sand cores are used, and mold design is nearly as elaborate as in sand casting. However, because the mold is made from cast iron and is used repeatedly with a satisfactory wash or coating each time, the process lends itself economically only to the production of thousands of castings. Permanent mold casting becomes less costly than sand casting in this range of production. In addition, there are certain quality advantages to the process. Some alloys develop finer grain size and thus higher mechanical properties when cast in the faster-freezing permanent mold. Uniformity of castings is usually greater than with sand casting. Surface finish is much smoother on permanent mold castings. Since the casting is removed by separating the mold into halves rather than by shakeout, there are more restrictions on the shape and location of gates and risers, which make the process a little less adaptable to the most complex shapes.

Pressure die casting allows the ultimate in the high-rate, high-volume, low-cost production of castings of slight to moderate volume and section thickness. The use of high hydrostatic pressure applied to the molten metal through a cylinder and ram permits the rapid and complete filling of the mold cavity with a minimum of accessory gate and sprue volume. Magnesium alloys are excellently suited to the manufacture of high-quality die castings at high production rates, to a large extent because of the very factors that complicate their sand casting—the low specific heat and low density.

There are two procedures for die casting, and machines corresponding to them. They are the cold-chamber and the hot-chamber processes. The cold-chamber operation is by far the most common in the United States. A fixed quantity of metal is poured into the chamber or shot well in front of the withdrawn pressure plunger with a hand ladle. The plunger is then moved through the chamber hydraulically at a rapid rate. The molten metal fills the die cavity under high hydrostatic pressure and solidifies rapidly in contact with the die walls, which are steel. The plunger is returned to its starting point, the die cavity is opened, and the casting is withdrawn. After a lubrication of the shot well itself, if necessary, the cycle is repeated. Production rate and uniformity of the casting are limited not only by the machine characteristics but also by the speed and consistency of the operation. Automatic metering arrangements may be attached to a cold-chamber machine, allowing an increase in reproducibility of casting quality as well as an increase in production rate.[39, 40]

The hot-chamber die-casting machine operates as shown in Fig. 6.10.[41] A well of the molten metal is directly connected with the die cavity. The pressure for the movement of metal into the cavity is from a plunger which operates partially or completely bathed in the liquid metal. Although the plunger in the cold chamber is in periodic

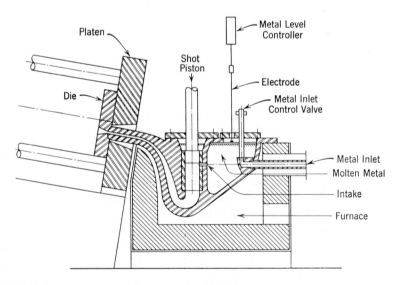

Fig. 6.10. The Dow hot-chamber machine for die-casting magnesium alloy.[41] Molten metal flows from the holding pot through the metal inlet to the reservoir. When shot piston is up (as shown), molten metal is admitted into the gooseneck shot chamber. Metal is forced into the cavity by the descending piston.

contact with the liquid, it does not have to stand the continuous erosion and heat of that in the hot-chamber machine. Thus the material and sealing requirements are much more stringent in the latter case. Tungsten alloy steel is used for the plunger in one design now available to the die caster of magnesium. The plunger of the cold-chamber machine, on the other hand, need only be fabricated from type H-13 steel. The alloy AZ91B is the most popular for die casting magnesium. The mechanical strength of AZ91B die castings is high; their corrosion resistance and soundness are satisfactory. The major problems in magnesium alloy die casting are hot-cracking and shrinkage. Mann's study of the die casting of several alloys and pure magnesium indicates that, the smaller the solidification temperature range interval is, the less the shrinkage and crack susceptibility.[42] AZ91 alloys have a fairly long solidification range (about 135°C) but, with proper die design, cracking is held to a minimum. Die temperature and holding time are also critical variables in the minimization of hot-cracking.

# References

1. T. E. Leontis, "New Magnesium Alloys for High Temperature," *Metal Progr.,* **72,** 97 (1957).
2. T. E. Leontis, "Uses of Thorium in Magnesium Technology," in *The Metal Thorium,* American Society for Metals, Cleveland, Ohio, 1958, Chapter 3, 29–56.
3. *Magnesium Design,* The Dow Chemical Company, Midland, Mich., 1957.
4. *"Elektron" Magnesium Alloys,* Magnesium Elektron Limited, Clifton Junction, Manchester, England, 1956.
5. T. E. Leontis and C. E. Nelson, "The Aging of Sand Cast Mg-Al-Zn Alloys," *Trans. AIME,* **191,** 120 (1951).
6. F. Sauerwald, "Der Stand der Entwicklung der Zwei- und Vielstofflegierungen auf der Basis Magnesium-Zirkon und Magnesium-Thorium-Zirkon," *Z. Metallk.,* **45,** 257 (1954).
7. F. Sauerwald, "Über die Beinflussung der Erstorrungskristallisation von Magnesiumlegierungen durch Zirkonium und einige Eigenschaften von gegossenen Magnesium-Legierungen mit Zirkonium," *Z. Metallk.,* **40,** 41 (1949).
8. C. J. P. Ball, "The History of Magnesium," *J. Inst. Metals,* **84,** 399 (1955–1956).
9. E. F. Emley, "Non-Metallic Inclusions in Magnesium Base Alloys Containing Zirconium," *J. Inst. Metals,* **75,** 481 (1948).
10. W. P. Saunders and F. P. Strieter, "Alloying Zirconium to Magnesium," *Trans. AFS,* **60,** 581 (1952).
11. J. Dornauf, "Zirkonhaltige Magnesiumlegierungen mit Zusätzen von Zink, Cer und Thorium, ihre Herstellung und Schmelz-technik," *Z. Metallk.,* **48,** 142 (1957).

12. T. E. Leontis, "The Room and Elevated Temperature Properties of Some Sand Cast Magnesium-base Alloys Containing Zinc," *Trans. AIME*, **180**, 287 (1949).

13. J. F. Hildebrand and F. P. Strieter, "Mechanical Properties of Sand Cast Mg-Zn-Zr Alloys," *Trans. AFS*, **60**, 595 (1952).

14. C. S. Roberts, "Interaction of Precipitation and Creep in Mg-Al Alloys," *Trans. AIME*, **206**, 146 (1956).

15. T. E. Leontis, "The Properties of Sand Cast Magnesium-Rare Earth Alloys," *Trans. AIME*, **185**, 968 (1949).

16. T. E. Leontis and D. H. Feisel, "Sand Cast Magnesium-Rare Earth Metal-Zirconium Alloys," *Trans. AIME*, **209**, 1245 (1957).

17. G. A. Mellor and R. W. Ridley, "The Creep Strength at 200°C of Some Magnesium Alloys Containing Cerium," *J. Inst. Metals*, **75**, 697 (1948).

18. G. A. Mellor and R. W. Ridley, "Creep at 250° and 300°C of Some Magnesium Alloys Containing Cerium," *J. Inst. Metals*, **81**, 245 (1953).

19. C. S. Roberts, "Creep Behavior of Magnesium-Cerium Alloys," *Trans. AIME*, **200**, 634 (1954).

20. K. E. Nelson and F. P. Strieter, "Casting of Magnesium-Rare Earth-Zirconium Alloys in Sand Molds," *Trans. AFS*, **68**, 400 (1950).

21. K. E. Nelson, "Magnesium Sand Casting Alloys Containing Thorium," *Trans. AFS*, **61** (1953).

22. C. J. P. Ball, A. C. Jessup, P. A. Fisher, D. J. Whitehead, and J. B. Wilson, "Further Progress in the Development of Mg-Zr Alloys to Give Good Creep and Fatigue Properties Between 500° and 650°F," *Trans. AIME*, **197**, 924 (1953).

23. K. E. Nelson, "The Properties of Sand Cast Mg-Th-Zn-Zr Alloys," *Trans. AIME*, **197**, 1493 (1953).

24. K. E. Nelson, "Foundry Characteristics and Properties of Magnesium Sand Casting Alloy HZ32XA," *Trans. AFS*, **63**, 596 (1955).

25. T. E. Leontis, "Properties of Magnesium-Thorium and Magnesium-Thorium-Cerium Alloys," *Trans. AIME*, **194**, 287 (1952).

26. T. E. Leontis, "Effect of Zirconium on Magnesium-Thorium and Magnesium-Thorium-Cerium Alloys," *Trans. AIME*, **194**, 633 (1952).

27. C. E. Nelson, "The Melting and Refining of Magnesium," *Trans. AIME*, **59**, 392 (1944).

28. E. F. Emley, "Non-Metallic Inclusions in Magnesium-Base Alloys and the Flux-Refining Process," *J. Inst. Metals*, **75**, 431 (1948).

29. J. Koeneman and A. G. Metcalfe, "The Solubility of Hydrogen in Magnesium," *Trans. ASM*, **51**, 1072 (1959).

30. E. J. Whittenberger and F. N. Rhines, "Origin of Porosity in Castings of Magnesium-Aluminum and Other Alloys, *Trans. AIME*, **194**, 409 (1952).

31. J. deHaven, J. A. Davis, and L. W. Eastwood, "Reduction of Microporosity in Magnesium Alloy Castings," *Trans. AFS*, **53**, 180 (1945).

32. R. S. Busk, R. F. Marande, and W. C. Newhams, "Effects of Gas on the Properties of Magnesium Sand Casting Alloys," *Trans. AFA*, **53**, 272 (1945).

33. L. Sturkey and T. L. Joseph, Jr., "Fundamental Study of Factors Affecting Grain Refinement in Common Magnesium Sand Casting Alloys," Final Report, Contract No. DA-20-018-RD-11663, The Dow Chemical Co., Midland, Mich., October 1953.

34. J. R. Burns, "Beryllium in Magnesium Casting Alloys," *Trans. ASM*, **40**, 143 (1948).
35. K. E. Mann, "The Effect of Extremely Low Be Contents in Magnesium Alloys," *Z. Metallk.*, **46**, 17 (1955).
36. H. E. Elliott, "Casting High Quality Magnesium," *Modern Castings and Am. Foundryman*, July 1955.
37. *Magnesium—Fabricating and Casting*, Organization for European Economic Cooperation, Paris, 1956.
38. H. E. Elliott, "Gating and Risering of Magnesium Alloys," *Am. Foundryman* (April and May 1954).
39. F. L. Burkett and F. C. Bennett, "Automatic Metering for Cold Chamber Die Casting," presented at AFS meeting, Cincinnati, Ohio, May 6–10, 1957.
40. F. L. Burkett, U. S. Patent No. 2,745,153 (May 15, 1956).
41. F. C. Bennett, "For Magnesium: A Hot Chamber Die Casting Machine," *Modern Metals* (December 1954).
42. K. E. Mann, "Shrinkage and Crack Susceptibility of Magnesium Pressure Die-Castings," *Giesserei*, **44**, 301 (1957).
43. A. W. Brace and F. A. Allen, *Magnesium Casting Technology*, Reinhold Publishing Corp., New York, 1957.
44. A. J. Murphy, *Non-Ferrous Foundry Metallurgy*, chapter on "Magnesium-Base Alloys" by F. A. Fox, McGraw-Hill Book Co., New York, 1954.
45. The Dow Chemical Company, "Crucible Melting of Magnesium Alloys," *Bulletin No. 141-27*.

# 7

# Wrought Alloys and Technology

## 7.1 Introduction

Abundant wrought products, i.e., rolled sheet or plate, extrusion, and forgings are necessary to establish large-scale structural applications of a metal in our modern technology. These worked forms have the advantage of lower cost, higher strengths, and ductilities as well as more versatility of mechanical properties than cast forms. Bold steps have been taken by the two major producers of magnesium mill products in the United States—The Dow Chemical Company and Brooks and Perkins. Dow's huge mill at Madison, Illinois, represents a capacity which will supply the nation's needs for many years. Brooks and Perkins, although primarily leading fabricators of magnesium assemblies from mill products, are producing their own sheet in increasing quantity. The development of capacity for mill production in other countries lags far behind the commitment that has been made by Dow. However, Domal in Canada and Magnesium Elektron Ltd. and Essex Aero Ltd. of Great Britain are active in the wrought-product market. The latter produces wrought products from secondary magnesium in an operation which is very economical and which allows some successful competition with the Dow production.

Fortunately the development of magnesium wrought products has been rather well balanced in extrusions, sheet, plate, and forgings. The metal is well adapted to all three working processes, especially to extrusion, where some rather progressive innovations have been made with magnesium. The ready availability of all forms at the time when designers are considering magnesium alloys more and more seriously has encouraged design versatility. The principal wrought magnesium alloys, their composition, and their mechanical properties in

Table 7.1. Chemical Composition of Wrought Magnesium Alloys

| ASTM Alloy | Chemical Composition, % | | | | | | | | | | | | |
|---|---|---|---|---|---|---|---|---|---|---|---|---|---|
| | Al | Mn, Min. | Zn | Zr | Rare Earths | Th | Ca | Si, Max. | Cu, Max. | Ni, Max. | Fe, Max. | Other Imp., Max. | Mg |
| AZ31B | 2.5–3.5 | 0.20 | 0.7–1.3 | — | — | — | 0.04 max. | 0.30 | 0.05 | 0.005 | 0.005 | 0.30 | Bal. |
| AZ31C | 2.5–3.5 | 0.20 | 0.6–1.4 | — | — | — | 0.04 max. | 0.30 | 0.10 | 0.03 | — | 0.30 | Bal. |
| AZ61A | 5.8–7.2 | 0.15 | 0.4–1.5 | — | — | — | — | 0.30 | 0.05 | 0.005 | 0.005 | 0.30 | Bal. |
| AZ80A | 7.8–9.2 | 0.15 | 0.2–0.8 | — | — | — | — | 0.30 | 0.05 | 0.005 | 0.005 | 0.30 | Bal. |
| M1A | — | 1.20 | — | — | — | — | 0.08–0.14 | 0.30 | 0.05 | 0.01 | — | 0.30 | Bal. |
| HM21A | — | 0.35–0.80 | — | — | — | 1.5–2.5 | — | — | — | — | — | 0.30 | Bal. |
| HM31A | — | 1.2 | — | — | — | 2.5–3.5 | — | — | — | — | — | 0.30 | Bal. |
| ZE10A | — | — | 1.0–1.5 | — | 0.12–0.22 | — | — | — | — | — | — | 0.30 | Bal. |
| ZK11 * | — | — | 1.3 | 0.7 | — | — | — | — | — | — | — | — | Bal. |
| ZK31 † | — | — | 3.0 | 0.7 | — | — | — | — | — | — | — | — | Bal. |
| ZK60A | — | — | 4.8–6.2 | 0.45 min. | — | — | — | — | — | — | — | 0.30 | Bal. |

* British alloy ZW1.
† British alloy ZW3.

Table 7.2.   Room-Temperature Mechanical Properties
of Magnesium Sheet and Plate

| Alloy | Temper | Thickness, in. | TS, 1000 psi | | TYS, 1000 psi | | Elongation in 2 in., % | | CYS, 1000 psi | |
|---|---|---|---|---|---|---|---|---|---|---|
| | | | Typ. | Min. | Typ. | Min. | Typ. | Min. | Typ. | Min. |
| AZ31B | -O | 0.016–0.060 | 37 | 32 | 22 | 18 | 21 | 12 | 16 | 12 |
| | | 0.061–0.250 | 37 | 32 | 22 | 15 | 21 | 12 | 16 | 12 |
| | | 0.251–0.500 | 37 | 32 | 23 | 15 | 23 | 12 | 15 | 10 |
| | | 0.501–2.000 | 37 | 30 | 23 | 15 | 17 | 10 | 14 | 10 |
| | -H24 | 0.016–0.064 | 42 | 39 | 32 | 29 | 15 | 4 | 26 | 25 |
| | | 0.065–0.250 | 42 | 39 | 32 | 29 | 15 | 4 | 26 | 24 |
| | | 0.251–0.500 | 39 | 37 | 27 | 24 | 18 | 10 | 21 | 14 |
| | | 0.501–1.000 | 38 | 37 | 24 | 22 | 19 | 10 | 16 | 12 |
| | | 1.001–1.500 | 37 | 35 | 24 | 21 | 18 | 8 | 15 | 11 |
| | | 1.501–2.000 | 36 | 34 | 23 | 19 | 15 | 8 | 13 | 10 |
| | -H26 | 0.251–0.375 | 42 | 37 | 31 | 26 | 9 | 6 | 23 | 21 |
| | | 0.376–0.438 | 41 | 37 | 30 | 26 | 9 | 6 | 21 | 19 |
| | | 0.439–0.500 | 40 | 37 | 29 | 26 | 9 | 6 | 20 | 18 |
| | | 0.501–0.750 | 40 | 37 | 28 | 25 | 10 | 8 | 19 | 17 |
| | | 0.751–1.000 | 39 | 37 | 26 | 23 | 10 | 8 | 18 | 16 |
| | | 1.001–1.500 | 38 | 35 | 25 | 22 | 10 | 8 | 16 | 15 |
| | | 1.501–2.000 | 37 | 34 | 24 | 20 | 10 | 8 | 15 | 14 |
| AZ31B | -H10 | 0.251–2.000 | 35 | 30 | 20 | 12 | 17 | 10 | 15 | 10 |
| | -H11 | 0.016–0.250 | 37 | 32 | 20 | 12 | 20 | 12 | 16 | 12 |
| | -H23 | 0.016–0.064 | 42 | 39 | 28 | 25 | 15 | 4 | 26 | 25 |
| | | 0.065–0.250 | 42 | 39 | 28 | 25 | 15 | 4 | 25 | 20 |
| HK31A | -H24 | 0.016–0.125 | 37 | 34 | 29 | 26 | 8 | 4 | 25 | 20 |
| | | 0.126–0.250 | 37 | 31 | 29 | 22 | 8 | 4 | 25 | 18 |
| | | 0.251 up | 31 | — | 23 | — | 15 | — | 22 | — |
| ZE10A | -H24 | 0.016–0.125 | 38 | 36 | 28 | — | 12 | 4 | 26 | — |
| | -H24 | 0.126–0.188 | 37 | 34 | 25 | — | 12 | 4 | 24 | — |
| | -H24 | 0.189–0.250 | 34 | 31 | 19 | — | 8 | 4 | 16 | — |
| | -O | 0.016–0.060 | 33 | 30 | 23 | — | 23 | 15 | 16 | — |
| | -O | 0.001–0.250 | 33 | 30 | 20 | — | 23 | 15 | 16 | — |
| | -O | 0.251–0.500 | 31 | 29 | 16 | — | 18 | 12 | 12 | — |
| HM21A | -TB | 0.016–0.125 | 34 | — | 25 | — | 10 | — | 15 | — |
| ZK11 * | -F | | 36 | — | 27 | — | 12 | — | — | — |
| ZK31 † | -F | | 38 | — | 29 | — | 12 | — | — | — |

* British Alloy ZW1.
† British Alloy ZW3.

### Table 7.3. Room-Temperature Mechanical Properties of Magnesium Bars, Rods, Shapes

| Alloy | Temper | Diameter or Thickness in Least Dimension, in. | TS, 1000 psi Typ. | Min. | TYS, 1000 psi Typ. | Min. | Elongation in 2 in., % Typ. | Min. | CYS, 1000 psi Typ. | Min. |
|---|---|---|---|---|---|---|---|---|---|---|
| AZ31B | -F | under 0.250 | 38 | 35 | 28 | 21 | 14 | 10 | 15 | — |
|  | -F | 0.250–1.499 | 38 | 35 | 29 | 22 | 15 | 10 | 14 | 12 |
|  | -F | 1.500–2.499 | 38 | 34 | 28 | 22 | 14 | 10 | 14 | 12 |
|  | -F | 2.500–5.000 | 38 | 32 | 28 | 20 | 15 | 7 | 14 | 10 |
| AZ61A | -F | under 0.250 | 46 | 38 | 33 | 20 | 17 | 8 | — | — |
|  | -F | 0.250–1.499 | 45 | 40 | 33 | 24 | 16 | 10 | 19 | 14 |
|  | -F | 1.500–2.499 | 45 | 40 | 33 | 24 | 16 | 10 | 19 | 14 |
|  | -F | 2.500–5.000 | 45 | 40 | 31 | 22 | 15 | 7 | 21 | 14 |
| AZ80A | -F | under 0.250 | 49 | 43 | 36 | 28 | 12 | 9 | — | — |
|  | -F | 0.250–1.499 | 49 | 43 | 36 | 28 | 11 | 9 | — | 17 |
|  | -F | 1.500–2.499 | 49 | 43 | 35 | 28 | 11 | 8 | — | 17 |
|  | -F | 2.500–5.000 | 48 | 42 | 36 | 27 | 9 | 4 | — | 17 |
|  | -T5 | under 0.250 | 55 | 47 | 38 | 30 | 8 | 5 | 34 | — |
|  | -T5 | 0.250–1.499 | 55 | 48 | 40 | 33 | 7 | 4 | 35 | 28 |
|  | -T5 | 1.500–2.499 | 53 | 48 | 39 | 33 | 6 | 4 | 32 | 27 |
|  | -T5 | 2.500–5.000 | 50 | 45 | 38 | 30 | 6 | 2 | 31 | 26 |
| M1A | -F | under 0.250 | 37 | 30 | 26 | — | 12 | 2 | 12 | — |
|  | -F | 0.250–1.499 | 37 | 32 | 26 | — | 11 | 3 | 12 | — |
|  | -F | 1.500–2.499 | 39 | 32 | — | — | 9 | 2 | — | — |
|  | -F | 2.500–5.000 | 38 | 29 | — | — | 5 | 2 | — | — |

| Alloy | Temper | Cross-Sect. Area | TS, 1000 psi Typ. | Min. | TYS, 1000 psi Typ. | Min. | Elongation in 2 in., % Typ. | Min. | CYS, 1000 psi Typ. | Min. |
|---|---|---|---|---|---|---|---|---|---|---|
| ZK60A | -F | less than 2 sq in. | 49 | 43 | 38 | 31 | 14 | 5 | 33 | 27 |
|  | -F | 2–3 sq in. | 49 | 43 | 37 | 31 | 14 | 5 | 28 | 26 |
|  | -F | 3–5 sq in. | 49 | 43 | 36 | 31 | 14 | 5 | 27 | 25 |
|  | -F | 5–40 sq in. | 48 | 43 | 37 | 31 | 9 | 4 | 23 | 20 |
|  | -T5 | less than 2 sq in. | 53 | 45 | 44 | 36 | 11 | 4 | 36 | 30 |
|  | -T5 | 2–3 sq in. | 52 | 45 | 43 | 36 | 12 | 4 | 31 | 28 |
|  | -T5 | 3–5 sq in. | 51 | 45 | 42 | 36 | 14 | 4 | 30 | 25 |
| HM31A | -F |  | 42 | — | 33 | — | 10 | — | 27 | — |

various forms are listed in Tables 7.1 to 7.5.[1,2] The same use is made of the ASTM designation system as in Chapter 6 (see p. 127). The compressive yield strength has been added to Table 7.2 to 7.5 because (a) unlike magnesium castings, where the compressive and tensile properties are invariably equal, the wrought products, primarily because of their preferred orientation, exhibit compressive yield strength which is generally lower than the tensile yield strength; and (b) in

### Table 7.4. Room-Temperature Mechanical Properties of Magnesium Tubing

| Alloy | Temper | Outside Diameter, max. in. | Wall Thickness Range, in. | TS, 1000 psi | | TYS, 1000 psi | | Elongation in 2 in., % | | CYS, 1000 psi | |
|---|---|---|---|---|---|---|---|---|---|---|---|
| | | | | Typ. | Min. | Typ. | Min. | Typ. | Min. | Typ. | Min. |
| AZ31B or AZ31C | -F | 6 | 0.028–0.250 | 36 | 32 | 24 | 16 | 16 | 8 | 12 | 10 |
| | | | 0.251–0.750 | — | 32 | — | 16 | — | 4 | — | 10 |
| AZ61A | -F | 6 | 0.028–0.750 | 41 | 36 | 24 | 16 | 14 | 7 | 16 | 11 |
| M1A | -F | 6 | 0.028–0.750 | 35 | 28 | 21 | — | 10 | 2 | 9 | — |
| ZK60A | -F | 3 | 0.028–0.750 | 46 | 40 | 34 | 28 | 12 | 5 | 25 | 20 |
| | -T5 | 3 | 0.028–0.750 | 50 | 46 | 40 | 38 | 11 | 4 | 29 | 26 |

### Table 7.5. Room-Temperature Mechanical Properties of Magnesium Forgings *

| Alloy | Temper | TS, 1000 psi | | TYS, 1000 psi | | Elongation in 2 in., % | | CYS, 1000 psi | |
|---|---|---|---|---|---|---|---|---|---|
| | | Typ. | Min. | Typ. | Min. | Typ. | Min. | Typ. | Min. |
| AZ31B | -F | 38 | — | 28 | — | 9 | — | 12 | — |
| AZ61A | -F | 43 | 38 | 26 | 22 | 12 | 6 | 17 | — |
| AZ80A | -F | 46 | 42 | 31 | 26 | 8 | 5 | 25 | — |
| | -T5 | 50 | 42 | 34 | 28 | 6 | 2 | 28 | — |
| | -T6 | 50 | — | 34 | — | 5 | — | 27 | — |
| M1A | -F | 36 | 30 | 23 | 18 | 7 | 3 | — | — |
| ZK60A | -T5 | 49 | — | 38 | — | 13 | — | 28 | — |

\* Data from outside specifications, World War II production data, and recent laboratory test data. Only longitudinal properties are given.

view of the importance of buckling in the typical design applications of wrought products, the compressive properties are often the critical ones.

Success in producing useful magnesium wrought products is controlled by the following factors:

1. Casting a fine and equiaxial grained ingot with a minimum of gross or local segregation of harmful phases and of satisfactory shape and volume for economy in the working process.

2. Accomplishing the initial *breakdown* or hot-working of the ingot to a recrystallized and reasonably fine-grained structure without cracking or other failure.

3. Finishing of the magnesium wrought product to dimensions with satisfactory tolerances, avoiding cracking and producing a fine-worked and/or recrystallized grain structure which allows the final mechanical properties to be present or obtainable with further suitable heat treatment.

To accomplish these things with the hexagonal close-packed alloys of magnesium, grain size of the ingot is controlled. In addition, the technologist keeps in mind the complications of the operation of twinning, the temperature dependence of nonbasal slip, and the importance of preferred orientation, which is developed early in the working schedule.

## 7.2 Magnesium-Manganese- and Magnesium-Aluminum-Based Wrought Alloys

M1A alloy, which in the form of extrusions, sheet, and plate has served as a low-cost, relatively low-strength magnesium wrought alloy for many years, has declined in use because of the higher properties consistently demanded in modern structural applications. It is a simple alloy to manufacture. The manganese addition is beneficial in controlling the iron content of the magnesium, and the alloy has very good corrosion resistance as a result. The strength of the alloy results primarily from grain refinement, cold-work, and possibly dispersion-hardening. The precipitation-hardening effect is so small that M1A is nonheat-treatable; i.e., no advantage is gained by heat-treating it. The British equivalent is AM503.

Alloys AZ31B and AZ31C, which differ only in the allowable impurity content, are the commercial wrought-product compositions of greatest importance in the present magnesium market. The American use of these alloys in the form of sheet, plate, and extrusions is matched by an almost equivalent versatility in Great Britain and Canada. The balance between strength and ductility of the AZ31 alloys is primarily one of controlling the work-hardening remaining in the sheet, extrusion, or forging after the fabrication operation and any other annealing that it receives intentionally or incidentally during the cooling to room temperature. Although some precipitation effects may be occurring in this composition, the primary function of the aluminum and zinc is to supply solid solution-hardening and grain refinement to the base magnesium. Probably no nominal composition has been studied more thoroughly than this one, and yet new and helpful information is constantly being brought out concerning its behavior. As can be seen in Table 7.2, the tensile yield strength of AZ31B sheet can be varied from 22,000 to 30,000 psi by decreasing the amount of cold-work left in the final product. The elongation varies correspondingly from about 10% to slightly over 20%.

The primary intermetallic phases in AZ31 alloys, $Mg_{17}Al_{12}$ and $Mg_3Al_2Zn_3$, are present in cast ingot. However, very little of either remains out of solution in the final AZ31 wrought products. Recent careful studies of these phases with the aid of electron diffraction by Sturkey have contributed greatly to an understanding of the secondary phases in AZ31 alloys.[3] The secondary phases which have been identified are $\alpha(MnAlSi)$, $Mn_6Al_7$, $MnAl_6$, and $Al_2Ca$. The principal one of the group is $\alpha(MnAlSi)$ which has the following characteristics:

1. Approximate composition $Mn_3SiAl_{12}$.
2. Cubic structure, $a_0 = 12.6$ A.
3. Flakelike habit on the (111) plane.
4. Usually not found in AZ31 sheet containing $<0.04\%$ Ca.
5. Usually found in AZ31 when Ca $> 0.04\%$ and Mn $> 0.06\%$.

The connection with calcium explains the specification of the maximum calcium content in the composition of AZ31B and AZ31C in Table 7.1. Early in the history of commercial AZ31 sheet and plate production, calcium additions in the range 0.1–0.16% were used to produce an alloy known as AZ31A. The higher calcium content makes the weldability of AZ31A inferior to that of AZ31B and AZ31C, and the former composition is no longer in commercial production. It seems clear that the higher calcium content in AZ31A does contribute some grain refinement, by a mechanism which is not completely understood, as well as higher final properties to the rolled sheet.

When manganese as well as calcium is held to a low level, rolled AZ31 sheet is produced which has excellent photoengraving characteristics. This alloy, which is known as PE, is produced commercially for the rapidly expanding market for magnesium photoengraving sheet in the printing industry. Since its performance is not controlled primarily by the mechanical properties but rather by its chemical etching characteristics, this alloy composition has not been standardized in ASTM specifications. PE sheet must contain as few secondary particles as possible that are insoluble in the acid etch used in the engraving process and must etch smoothly without undercutting. The iron content is kept low to prevent serious corrosion during storage.

When the calcium content of AZ31 sheet is held below 0.04%, the principal secondary phase is $Mn_6Al_7$ according to Sturkey and Moe. This is almost cubic in structure with $a_0$ approximately 9.0 A. When the calcium content is greater than 0.04%, $Al_2Ca$ is normally present in cast material in addition to the $\alpha$(MnAlSi) phase discussed above. $Al_2Ca$ is of the $Cu_2Mg$ (cubic C15) structure with a lattice parameter of 8.02 A. It is not found in thin-rolled sheet.

The last of the secondary phases that have been identified, $MnAl_6$, occurs to some extent in all AZ31 alloys containing more than 0.05% manganese. It is orthorhombic with $a = 6.4978$ A, $b = 7.5518$ A and $c = 8.8703$ A. It usually occurs as long needles or ribbons which may be oriented with the long axis in the rolling plane during the rolling operation.

AZ61A is primarily an extrusion and forging alloy of excellent strength and ductility. It is rarely supplied in sheet form, since the increased aluminum content makes rolling without cracking much more difficult than in the AZ31 group. Although an adequate amount of aluminum is present to allow improvement of properties by precipitation heat treatment, the cold-working, grain-refining, and solution-hardening characteristics are relied upon in practice to obtain high strength. The British counterpart of this alloy is called AZM by its manufacturer, Magnesium Elektron Ltd.

Until the advent of the Zn-Zr-based alloys, AZ80A offered the best combination of high tensile strength and moderate elongation available in commercial magnesium extrusion and forging compositions. It is still a fairly important structural alloy, since its principal ingredients are relatively low-cost, stably priced metals. Precipitation heat treatment may be used with AZ80A to give improvement in both tensile yield and tensile strengths with relatively little loss in ductility. A British equivalent is known as AZ855 and is restricted to forging applications.

## 7.3 Magnesium-Zinc-Based Wrought Alloys

The attainment of reasonably fine equiaxial grains in the cast ingot to be used for working magnesium alloys to a wrought form is as important as it is in the case of the casting alloys. Although the potent strengthening capacity of zinc in magnesium was attractive for use in wrought alloys for many years, as in the casting technology, the use of this system awaited the entrance of practical alloying of zirconium to magnesium. Zirconium, with its grain-refining and strengthening characteristics, was a logical introduction to wrought alloys following its original application in the casting technology (see Section 6.3). As in the case of the cast alloys, it is not compatible with aluminum or manganese, but, when they are used as alloying ingredients, grain refinement is obtained without its use. However, all commercial alloys which do not contain these elements in significant quantity do contain zirconium. It has had a great impact on the technology of wrought magnesium alloys.

The development of the extrusion alloy ZK60A in the Dow laboratories heralded the beginning of a new phase in magnesium wrought alloy design.[4] Examination of Tables 7.3 to 7.5 shows how much of an advantage over Mg-Al-based extrusions and forgings is obtained in ZK60A. Precipitation heat treatment brings tensile yield strengths over 40,000 psi with compressive yield strengths over 30,000 psi, while elongations remain above 10%. This tensile yield strength corresponds on an equal strength-to-weight basis to over 60,000 psi in an aluminum-based wrought alloy. Only one such alloy is available, the famous 7075 (formerly 75S) aluminum alloy in the heat-treated and aged condition. ZK60A rapidly found large-scale applications in the aircraft field soon after its commercial debut. A British equivalent is known as ZW6.

Although American manufacturers have restricted their commercial application of this system to extrusions and forgings, the British magnesium industry has turned to the use of Mg-Zn-based alloy sheet as well as extrusions and forgings in their attempt to build their market for wrought products. Two compositions, corresponding to ASTM designations ZK31 and ZK11, and termed ZW3 and ZW1 respectively by the manufacturer, are offered in the form of sheet as well as extrusions. The properties of these alloys in sheet form, as shown in Table 7.2, are comparable with those of AZ31B.

The Zn-Zr-containing alloys are relatively expensive compared to the Mg-Al-based group, primarily because of the cost of zirconium and zinc. However, on a strength per unit cost basis, Mg-1% Zn is the cheapest alloy possible at present metal prices. This is another manifestation of the potent hardening characteristics of zinc when added to magnesium.[5, 6] Using this as a basis, Dow has developed the low-cost alloy ZE10A. It has better tensile properties than M1A but poorer tensile properties than AZ31B. All tests which indicate comparative toughness place ZE10A not only above AZ31B but also above all other magnesium alloy sheet. Like M1A but unlike AZ31B, ZE10A is insensitive to stress-corrosion cracking after welding. Stress-relief treatments may be eliminated as a result.

## 7.4  Magnesium-Thorium-Based Wrought Alloys

The great demand for light wrought alloys as well as castings for service at elevated temperatures has led to the development of sheet and extrusion alloys in this category.  One of the important advantages of a wrought product is the strength that is based on its fine grain size and its degree of work-hardening.  During elevated-temperature exposure, the tendency for grain growth and recrystallization acts to deteriorate these advantageous alloy conditions.  It has been found that both rare-earth-metal additions and thorium additions block the grain growth, the tendency for recrystallization, and the potential grain boundary deformation that may result from such changes.  Although these effects are not completely understood, it seems probable that they result from a combination of the tendency of both the rare earth metals and thorium to (a) harden the solid solution; (b) raise the "recrystallization temperature" of the solid solu-

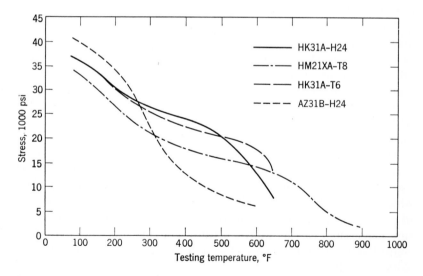

Fig. 7.1.  Temperature dependence of the tensile strength of magnesium alloy sheet of 0.040–0.250-in. thickness.[9]

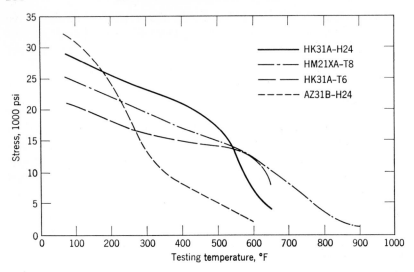

Fig. 7.2.  Temperature dependence of the tensile yield strength of magnesium alloy sheet of 0.040–0.250-in. thickness.[9]

tion; and (c) precipitate in the alloy with kinetics and microscopic location such as to reduce the deterioration of the mechanical properties at elevated temperature.[7,8]

The temperature dependence of some of the properties of several magnesium high-temperature wrought alloys are shown in Figs. 7.1 to 7.8.[9]  The behavior of the Mg-Al-based "room temperature" alloys are shown in the same figures for comparison.  It can be seen that the thorium-containing alloys extend the useful range of magnesium in structures up to about 370°C (700°F) at present.  However, the Mg-Al-based alloys should not be overlooked for application in the range up to 150°C (300°F).

Although much development work was done on the extruded magnesium–rare-earth-metal alloys,[10] they have not found a commercial use.  They were essentially eclipsed by the thorium-containing alloys which are equally strong at higher temperatures.  The whole sequence of development was more rapid than in the case of the high-temperature magnesium casting alloys, because alloying problems were under control and both rare earth metals and thorium were no longer "curiosities" as alloying elements.

The first and still the most important sheet alloy in the group is HK31A-H24.  This alloy is simply the cold-worked equivalent of the high-temperature casting alloy of the same composition. Its outstanding short-time properties up to 315°C (600°F) have brought it into mass production to supply the aircraft and missile market. Solution heat treatment and aging offer an improvement in the short-time properties above 260°C (500°F) but not below. Creep properties appear to be improved at all temperatures by heat treatment.

A systematic study at Dow of the high-temperature properties of Mg-Th-X alloys led to developments in the interesting Mg-Th-Mn system. The first commercial result was the extrusion alloy HM31XA, which extends the service range of magnesium extrusions to the region of 370°C (700°F), as shown in Figs. 7.5 to 7.8. Both the short-time and the creep properties are far superior to those of any other magnesium extrusion alloy. The strength of this alloy is controlled by a very stable state of precipitation and cold-work which resists thermal decay outstandingly. Therefore, heat treatment is ineffective in improving the mechanical properties.

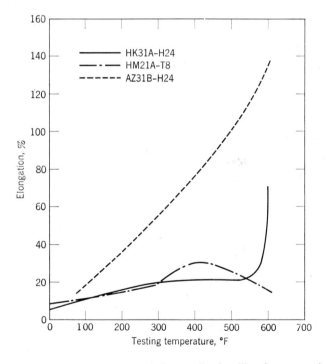

Fig. 7.3. Temperature dependence of the tensile ductility for magnesium alloy sheet.

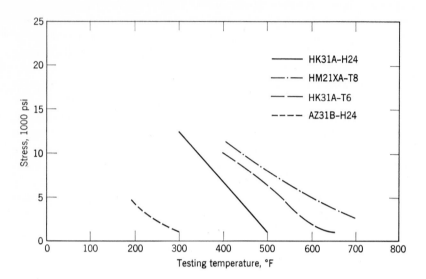

Fig. 7.4.  Temperature dependence of the creep limit for 0.2% total extension in 100 hr.  Magnesium alloy sheet of 0.064–0.250-in. thickness.[9]

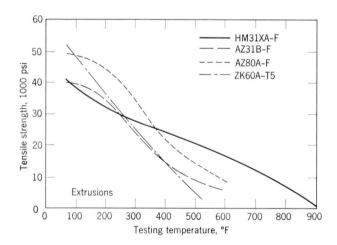

Fig. 7.5.  Temperature dependence of tensile strength of magnesium alloy extrusions.[9]

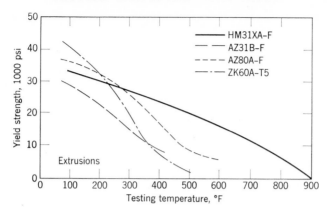

Fig. 7.6. Temperature dependence of tensile yield strengths of magnesium alloy extrusions.[9]

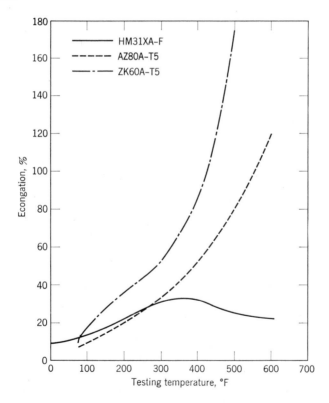

Fig. 7.7. Temperature dependence of tensile ductility of magnesium alloy extrusions.

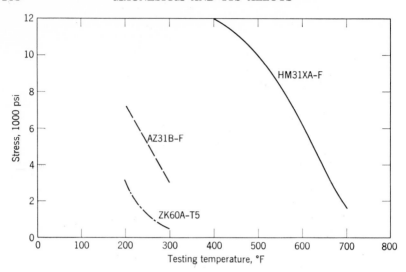

Fig. 7.8. Temperature dependence of the creep limit for 0.2% total extension in 100 hr. Magnesium alloy extrusions.[9]

The corresponding sheet alloy in the Th-Mn group is HM21A-T8. At temperatures above 315°C (600°F) it is the strongest magnesium alloy known in short-time tensile testing. It demonstrates a superiority in creep at even lower temperatures. It appears to have reasonably useful properties in the range of 425–480°C (800–900°F)!

## 7.5   Production of Ingot

Melting procedures for the primary ingot foundry are essentially the same as those described in Section 6.7 except in the amount of metal handled and the means of transferring it. Melting, alloying, and holding pot capacities are generally in the range of thousands of pounds of molten metal. An ingenious metal pumping system is used in the Dow primary metal foundry to avoid the use of transfer pots, crucibles, or tilting furnaces. Vertical spindle centrifugal pumps are immersed in the pots of molten magnesium alloy. The output of these pumps is fed from pot to pot and eventually to the casting station through ordinary iron pipe. The pumps are driven by compressed-air motors at a rate which is controllable by a hand valve on the air line, usually at the delivery end of the line. These transfer systems allow the convenient and troublefree transfer of over 1000 lb of magnesium alloy per minute. An electric current is passed through the iron pipelines to heat them adequately. In some cases gas flames are used as a more localized substitute for the electric heating.

Rolling and extrusion ingot were produced exclusively in the permanent mold for many years in the magnesium industry. Small experimental or pilot plant lots of ingot are still produced most efficiently in the split permanent mold. However, for large-scale operations of the modern continuous rolling mill and the high-capacity extrusion plant, the direct-chill continuous-casting operation allows better economy, quality control, and continuity of production.[11] The Dow company spent a long period of time and a large amount of money to adapt this process to the casting of magnesium alloys. A diagram of the equipment is shown in Fig. 7.9. A hollow cylindrical copper or aluminum mold is cooled with water spray or water jackets on its outer surface. Molten magnesium alloy is fed into the top of this mold to a constant level. This level is maintained by a simple servo system which senses with the length of an arc between a fixed probe and the surface of the melt, and which controls the air motor speed on the pump in the final delivery line. The clearance and the metal shrinkage upon freezing are such that the ingot, which is supported on the floor below the casting operation, moves freely down through the mold under control of the feed rollers at a rate which is equal to the pouring rate. The ingot is essentially completely frozen by the time it leaves the bottom of the mold. A flying circular saw automatically starts a cut when the end of the ingot has fallen the proper distance below it. The saw moves down with the ingot as it completes the cut and then returns to its starting point to prepare for the next cut. A deflector plate under the molten metal intake allows reduction of melt turbulence effect and distributes the melt with radial symmetry.

The ingot for extrusion work is round, and the typical rolling ingot shape is flat with half-round ends. Both are accomplished with relative ease in the continuous-casting process. The size of ingot produced on this type of equipment has increased steadily to the size now being used in the Dow plant at Madison, 41 in. wide, 13 in. thick, and 76 in. long for rolling ingot. Cylindrical ingot is cast for extrusion stock. Samples are normally taken from the ingot at this stage for checking grain size, cleanliness, and the absence of any cracking. The importance of control of the secondary phase condition in the ingot was discussed in Section 7.2.

The quality of the surface to be rolled or extruded is very important in determining the final surface condition of the wrought magnesium

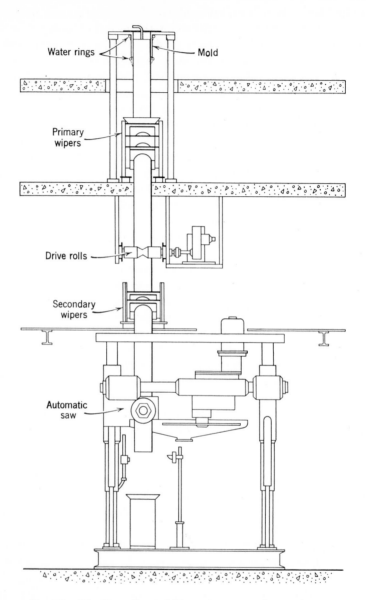

Fig. 7.9. The Dow direct-chill continuous-casting equipment.

alloy product as well as in controlling the tendency for cracking to occur during the working process. Therefore, the outer $\frac{1}{2}$-in. skin of the chill-cast ingot which may be irregular, folded, and somewhat segregated is removed with a milling machine or lathe before the metal is worked. This operation is known as scalping.

## 7.6    The Rolling of Magnesium Alloy

Hot-rolling is used as the initial stage to take advantage of the large reductions that are possible without cracking difficulties and, thus, to reduce the number of passes and reheats necessary to break down the cast structure and to produce a plate thin enough to finish-roll. The temperature of the metal ranges from 300 to 450°C, depending upon the alloy. Extruded slab was used to feed the rolling mill in early practice, but this procedure is not economical to mass-produce sheet and does not provide any improvement in properties.[12,13] In modern practice the ingot is "soaked" at temperature for several hours in a gas-heated furnace. Some manufacturers have heated the rolls for the hot-rolling operation, but this has become very impractical as larger mills have been introduced to the technology. At present, in the Madison practice, no separate roll-heating is being used. In general, roll-lubrication is used during the later stages of hot-breakdown.

Reductions per pass in hot-rolling of magnesium alloys range from 10 to 30%, and the number of reheats necessary to accomplish this from none to several, depending on the alloy. The typical hot-rolling schedule for AZ31B in the Madison operation is as follows:

Slab breakdown—metal temperature 455°C (850°F), approximately 10% reduction per pass to about $\frac{1}{4}$-in. coil.

Coil rundown—metal temperature 340°C (650°F), approximately 25% reduction per pass to prefinish gauge.

The cross-rolling passes which are used on the enormous ingot in the 84-in. hot mill are necessary to allow the production of final sheet 6 ft wide.

The ingot, approximately 12 in. thick after scalping, is reduced to the final thickness of 0.20 in. in 10 to 20 passes without intermediate heating. Mill speed is about 600 ft/min. The hot-rolled sheet is coiled on the final pass and allowed to cool to room temperature. The final pass is somewhat critical in that the combined effect of the sheet temperature in the rolls and the annealing which occurs during the cooling after coiling influences the final grain size of the hot-rolled sheet. This grain size must be small enough and uniform enough to allow the cold-rolling or finishing steps to proceed without cracking difficulties. Some mill products, such as tread plate and tooling plate, are finished hot. Economy of production, absence of residual stress, maximum machinability, and good weldability are more important here than are outstanding mechanical properties.

"Warm-rolling" with intermediate annealing is used to produce most of the sheet of less than 0.2-in. thickness and all of the sheet of less than 0.05-in. thickness. As in the breakdown operation, coil mills are used successfully at Madison. Once again care is necessary to monitor the effect of twinning on the compression side of the coiled magnesium sheet. Great material-handling economies result from the use of coil-rolling. A typical finishing schedule to give the maximum combination of mechanical properties, dimensional accuracy, and stability as well as surface quality in AZ31B as produced at Madison is as follows:

Metal temperature 260°C (500°F), reduction 25% in one pass. Anneal 135°C (275°F).

The characteristic cracking of sheet in the finishing stage is the formation of edge cracks which can extend across the width to form actually individual strips of metal. These are the shear cracks which are inclined to the sheet surface at the same angle as the compression bands discussed in Section 4.4. Apparently the cracking results from an overhardening of these bands and a failure along them in shear.

During the hot-breakdown operation, other characteristic cracking problems not peculiar to magnesium can present themselves to the inexperienced roller of magnesium alloy. Early in the process, the ingot may split along the neutral axis, a phenomenon which is called "alligatoring." This may be more an effect of the original cast structure than of recrystallized metal since it usually occurs before complete recrystallization can have occurred. Segregation of solutes during the freezing of the ingot, inadequate scalping of the ingot surface, or the existence of the secondary phases in the cast structure, as discussed in Section 7.2, may all contribute to alligatoring. Other problems during the hot-rolling operation are the occurrence of irregular edge cracking, which may result from inadequate edge scalping, pronounced segregation at the edge of the ingot, troublesome secondary phases, or simply the rapid cooling of the edge during the breakdown.

Roll condition and lubrication are important in the finishing of magnesium alloy sheet. Extensive empirical development has led to knowledge which is used at the Madison mill to reduce greatly the occasional problems with the cracking of sheet. These developments have much proprietary content and therefore cannot be described completely here. Although most magnesium alloys are rolled with a water solution lubricant, in some cases emulsions and so-called soluble oils are also used. The solute and additive concentrations are controlled to provide the desired degree of roll-cooling, friction reduction, and pickup prevention. The inherent disadvantages of emulsion-type rolling lubricants are absent in a water solution, and excellent sheet finish as well as significant economies are realized.

There is a distinct limit to the reduction that may be applied in the cold-rolling of AZ31B sheet before cracking occurs. This limit is about 30%. However, there is a group of magnesium alloys which has unlimited cold-rollability under proper rolling conditions. This group of alloys, about which much interest has centered at The Dow Chemical Company, is summarized by McDonald.[14] The effect has been observed in binary alloys containing calcium, zirconium, thorium, or the rare earth metals, and in ternary and polynary alloys containing combinations of these elements with or without manganese. The rolling conditions under which the effect is observed are rather restricted. The ratio of roll diameter to starting thickness must be large (about 50:1) and the reduction per pass must be small (about 2%). The mechanical property variations with increasing amounts of cold reduction are somewhat anomalous. The results of a study of this effect have been published by Couling, Pashak, and Sturkey.[15] A typical behavior is illustrated in Fig. 7.10 which summarizes their data for a Mg-0.2% mischmetal-0.4% Zr alloy (EK00). This alloy was hot-rolled to a thickness of 0.125 in. and cold-rolled in a mill with steam-heated rolls. Reduction was 1–2% per pass, the metal being reversed 180° in a vertical plane in the rolling direction between passes. The tensile yield strength of specimens cut from the sheet shows a moderate increase up to about 15% reduction. It shows a continuous decrease with greater reductions.

Aging the cold-rolled sheet at 205°C (400°F) results in an increase in the tensile yield strength in the region where the decrease has been observed with increasing cold reduction. The above-mentioned authors have developed an understanding of the mechanism of these anomalous effects with the help of careful metallography under polarized light and electron diffraction. Figure 4.8 illustrates the bands which they observed in the cross section of rolled sheet of Mg-0.5% Th (HO), the second alloy in which they observed the effects in Fig. 7.10.

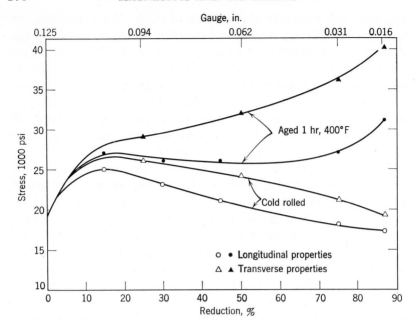

Fig. 7.10. Tensile yield strength of cold-rolled EKOO as a function of percent reduction.[15]

No recrystallization was observable in these bands, an observation which is consistent with the knowledge that both alloys have recrystallization temperatures under these working conditions of about 500°F as compared with that of AZ31B which is about 300°F. However, the polarized light showed quantitatively that the material within the bands was reoriented to a parallelism of the basal plane to the plane of the band, as had been shown in the pioneer work on these bands by Ernst and Laves.[16] Thus the resulting sheet would be expected to have a lower yield strength in longitudinal tension, where the resolved shear stress on the softer bands is higher than in transverse tension, where the shear stress is lower. Comparison of the longitudinal and transverse properties in Fig. 7.10 shows this to be true. The tensile strength and the elongation of the EK00 sheet showed trends which are consistent with that of the tensile yield strength. As was stated in Section 4.4, the authors have reason to doubt the mechanism originally put forth by Ernst and Laves, i.e., that the band formation is caused by a mechanism of fracture and rewelding, in view of the absence of recrystallization. The double twinning mechanism de-

scribed in that section seems a more likely explanation of this softening effect. Further work is needed to clarify the issue.

The easiest explanation of the hardening effect during aging was
the operation of precipitation of a solute-rich phase in the bands.
Two pieces of information obtained by Couling, Pashak, and Sturkey
disprove this interpretation. First, in the diffraction studies of aged
sheet, no increase in precipitate phase was found. Furthermore, the
aging effects were observed at temperatures where the known solubili-
ties of the rare earth metals and thorium were greater than the amount
present in the alloys. Second, the aging effect cycled with the softening effect, as is shown in Fig. 7.11. This behavior could hardly be explained in terms of precipitation process. Although they had no direct
evidence to support their hypothesis, the authors explained the aging
effect in terms of a possible polygonization followed by a solute pin-
ning of dislocation walls in the bands. Such a mechanism would allow
the nearly complete restorative effects, shown in Fig. 7.11, to occur.

The potential practical value of these anomalous effects is still a
matter of speculation and preliminary experimentation. The increased

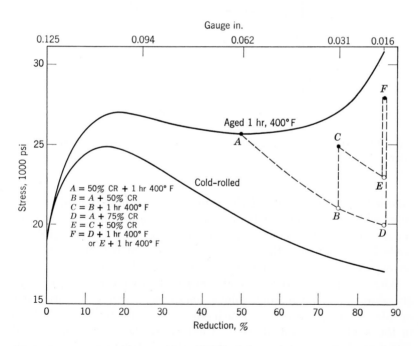

Fig. 7.11. Tensile yield strength of EKOO after alternate rolling and aging
treatments.[15]

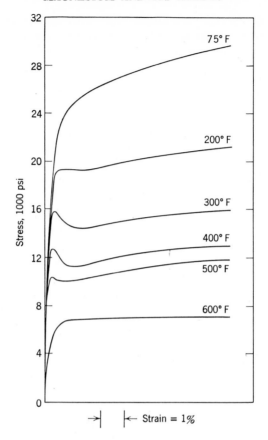

Fig. 7.12.  Tensile stress-strain curves at various temperatures for Mg-0.5% Th alloy.[17]

knowledge of the details of the compressive deformation of magnesium, which the studies for these alloys has afforded, may lead to more commercially valuable developments than the exact effects just described.  At any rate, the primary importance of banding in the deformation of polycrystalline magnesium is established.

When testing is carried out at elevated temperatures, yield points are observed in magnesium alloys containing thorium or rare earth metals.  Couling has reported such observations for the HO alloy used in the study discussed above.[17]  Cold-rolled sheet was annealed at 650°F producing a fine-grained recrystallized structure.  Stress-strain curves were obtained at 75, 200, 300, 400, 500, and 600°F.  As shown in Fig. 7.12, clear yield points were observed at 300, 400, and 500°F, none were seen at 75 and 600°F, and a faint indication of discontinuous yielding was seen at 200°F. Luders bands were observed on the specimen surfaces when yield points occurred. Unloading, aging at 400°F, and retesting at 300°F recaptured the yield point. The temperature dependence is explained by the incidence of enough additional deformation mechanisms at elevated temperature to allow the homogeneous deformation which is thought to be essential to the propagation of Luders bands.

## 7.7  The Extrusion of Magnesium

The extrusion of magnesium is not greatly different from the extrusion of other metals. Certain aspects of the deformation of magnesium alloys and some progressive developments in the industry allow it to show more versatility in extrusion than other metals enjoy at present. The pronounced temperature dependence of plastic deformation allows a wide mechanical range of properties to be obtained by varying the working temperature from the hot-extrusion range, where the wrought product is essentially completely recrystallized to the cold-extrusion region where a great deal of cold-work remains in the material. The latter operating region, where deformation occurs somewhat below the recrystallization temperature, is designed to produce high mechanical properties. This is a contrast to the technology of aluminum and steel, where extrusion is primarily a shaping operation and the resultant metal is heat-treatable for high mechanical properties.

Standard extrusion presses are used for commercial production ranging in available force from 1700 to 13,200 tons. The latter is the largest capacity yet applied to magnesium. Direct extrusion rather than indirect is used almost exclusively except in one special application. The ingot is regularly scalped (surface layer removed by machining) for this reason as well as to remove the highly segregated layer on the surface. Containers and dies are kept smooth by inspection, acid pickling, and/or polishing when necessary. The diameter of the cylindrical ingot or pre-extruded billet (more economical in the case of the smaller sizes) used on a press of a given capacity is determined by the maximum starting pressure that may be needed in the process. In general this is greatest at the start of the extrusion and is, of course, much higher for cold extrusion than for hot extrusion.

The primary commercial extrusion alloys, as shown in Tables 7.3 and 7.4 are AZ31B, AZ61A, AZ80A, M1A, ZK60A, and HM31XA. Direct-chill continuously cast material is used for raw material in the 13,200- and 5500-ton presses (16- or 32-in.-diameter ingot). The smaller presses are generally charged in practice at The Dow Chemical Company with pre-extruded billet which has been produced on the larger machines. Scalping is necessary only in the preparation of the original cast ingot. Continuous extrusion, i.e., insertion of a new ingot or billet to weld onto the butt of the previously extruded one, is generally practiced commercially in the United States. Longitudinal slots are machined in the ingot and extruded into the billet for the purpose of avoiding air release problems in continuous-extrusion processes.

Reductions in cross-section area range up to several hundred, depending upon the power available in the press and the properties desired in the extrusion. In general, it is desirable to have a reduction of at least 50 in commercial extrusion for complete breakup of the cast structure to be accomplished. As can be seen in Tables 7.3 and 7.4, better property combinations occur in the smaller extruded shapes for this reason. Pre-extruded billet as raw material allows somewhat lower reduction ratios than cast ingot, since a large amount of plastic deformation has occurred already.

The pronounced temperature dependence of plastic deformation in magnesium alloys allows a wide range of properties to be obtained by varying the working temperature from the hot-extrusion range, in the vicinity of 400°C (750°F), where the wrought product is essentially recrystallized to the cold-extrusion region, usually below 300°C (570°F), where a great deal of cold-work remains in the material. Since the metal is constrained hydrostatically in the container and the die, greater cold reductions in the cross-sectional area are possible than in the case of the rolling process. However, because of the severe one-stage reduction, much heat is developed in the die, both from the deformation of the metal and from the friction of it with the die and container walls. This developed heat increases with the extrusion speed. If it cannot be dissipated rapidly enough, the solidus of the alloy is exceeded, and failure of the extrusion surface by cracking will occur. Extrusion speeds of a few feet per minute are used for the highly alloyed materials (AZ80A, ZK60A, and HM31A). M1 and AZ31 alloys may be extruded at from 25 to several hundred feet per minute. The container and die temperatures are deliberately held lower than that of the metal at the start to help to control the problem of developed heat.

Early German work on the flow of magnesium in the extrusion process showed the same general characteristics that equivalent work on other metals both before and after have shown.[18] Unalloyed magnesium was alternated with layers of Mg-5% Zn alloy in an arrangement which took advantage of the differential staining tendencies of the two materials. The phenomenon of cavity entrance from the rear of the billet into the center of the extrusion was studied. The relatively minor influence of the shape of the pressure plate was examined also. The increase of both strength and elongation with increasing reduction in extrusion of high-aluminum-content alloys, a trend that is observable in Table 7.3, was discovered. Schmidt also emphasized the fine-grained skin as contrasted with the coarser-grained core, a condition which is characteristic of many magnesium alloy extrusions. The pronounced segregation of aluminum to the skin in the case of the high-aluminum alloys was also pointed out.

Hollow shapes in magnesium extrusions are usually produced with the two piece or spider die. The principle of operation is the breaking of the metal flow into three or four separate streams at the die entrance and their rewelding at the exit to a tube or other hollow shape. Piercing or drilling and the use of a mandrel are also practiced fairly extensively.

The novel and important development of a commercially feasible process for using magnesium alloy powder as the raw material for extrusion has been accomplished by Busk and Leontis of Dow.[19] An atomizing process was developed to produce the powder by breaking a thin stream of molten metal into droplets. Particles of the order of 350 $\mu$ average particle diameter are produced. The powder is then carefully preheated under protective atmosphere before it is charged into the press container. The powder extrusion process obtains better mechanical properties, more versatility of alloying, and therefore special combinations of other properties.

Since the strength, particularly the compressive yield strength, of magnesium alloy wrought products is especially susceptible to increase by refining the grain size, the developers of the powder extrusion process realized that they might gain improved properties if the amount of coring (local segregation) in the extrusion were increased and the scale over which this coring existed were reduced. The result should be a finer grain size. The atomized powder has the characteristic of pronounced coring over a very fine scale. Thus it is not surprising that the differences between the strength of conventional AZ31 extrusions and powder AZ31 extrusions as shown in Table 7.6 are so pro-

## Table 7.6.*   Variation of AZ31 Extrusion Properties
### with Billet Material [10]

| Type of Billet | Longitudinal, 1000 Psi | | | | Transverse, 1000 Psi | | | |
|---|---|---|---|---|---|---|---|---|
| | % Elon-gation | TYS | CYS | TS | % Elon-gation | TYS | CYS | TS |
| Solution heat-treated, direct cast | 14 | 20 | 12 | 35 | 3 | 23 | 12 | 37 |
| Direct as-cast | 19 | 25 | 21 | 39 | 11 | 28 | 21 | 39 |
| Atomized powder | 21 | 30 | 28 | 43 | 10 | 31 | 25 | 42 |

* Rectangle (3 in. $\times$ $\frac{1}{2}$ in.) extruded from 4-in. container at 700°F, 5 ft/min.

nounced.   The lower properties from the solution heat-treated billet also illustrate the coring principle above.

The powder extrusion process allows the mixtures of alloys having combined characteristics which are desired in the final extrusion. Busk and Leontis used AZ31 alloy as the base for their first work on the process.   They found that the product from powder had little of the fibrous characteristics of normal extrusions and that the compressive yield strength was much higher than is usual for this alloy.   When aluminum and zirconium were mixed into the charge in the form of KO alloy and Mg-Al eutectic respectively, a new hardening effect which was termed "interference hardening" occurred.   It appears that the zirconium and aluminum form an insoluble phase.   Thus a phenomenon which prevents the use of these two elements together in the normal cast-metal technology favors their practical use in the powder extrusion process.   The coextrusion of the AZ31 with M1 alloy contributed a large increase in resistance to stress-corrosion, an undesirable phenomenon pronounced in Mg-Al-Zn alloys but minimized in the Mn-containing alloy.   However, at least 50% M1 is added, with the sacrifice of some strength.   If 12% of Mg-Al eutectic is added, the "interference hardening" effect retains the properties as well as the extrudability.   The stress-corrosion properties are improved at the same time because of the manganese alloy addition.

## 7.8    The Forging of Magnesium Alloys

Although the modern press- and hammer-forging of metals represent the development of the oldest methods of plastically forming solid metal to useful shapes, magnesium alloys have been slow to find an application in the field. This situation appears to arise more from neglect than from any basic difficulty in the forging of magnesium. Traditionally, in the technology of all metals, casting and forging have found themselves in frequent competition for the manufacture of an intricate part, and the magnesium industry is no exception. Here, also, the design engineer must compare the property advantages of the two products. Usually higher strength and ductility as well as greater soundness can be obtained in the forging. However, the strength properties of the forging are very directional, whereas little such variation is found in the casting. Requirements in surface finish and cost are generally met about equally in the magnesium industry by the two fabrication techniques, if a reasonably large number of parts is produced. There are many complicated or re-entrant surface configurations which can be produced by casting but which can not be forged. The significance of the competition between magnesium castings and forgings is nicely illustrated by the aircraft wheel market, where forging has finally gained the edge on the foundry.

Most magnesium parts are made by press-forging, although hammer-forging may be used with M1A, AZ31B, and ZK60A alloys. A Mg-5% Sn-3% Al alloy (TA54) was at one time an important hammer-forging alloy. However, this composition is extremely susceptible to corrosion difficulties, and it is now of historical interest only. The important alloys for press-forging are ZK60A, AZ80A, AZ61A, AZ31B, and M1A, in order of decreasing strength. The first two alloys are outstanding in their strength. The advantages of ZK60A over the high-aluminum alloys are its greater elongation in tension and its better forgeability. It is outstanding in its toughness in forgings as well as in extrusions. Both ZK60A and AZ80A are used in the -T5 condition. Occasionally, in order to improve creep resistance, AZ80A is used in the -T6 condition. The other forging alloys are used without heat treatment. Typical properties of magnesium forgings are presented in Table 7.5.

Certain peculiarities are associated with the forging of magnesium alloys. The flow of metal is primarily lateral rather than longitudinal, upward or downward. Control of metal temperature is a bit more stringent than in many other metals. Forging metal temperatures are generally in the region of 400°C (750°F), with an allowable working range of 25° to 50°C. In general, because of the importance of cold-work in establishing part or all of the strength, especially in the more lowly alloyed materials, care is taken to finish at a low enough temperature to maintain the properties needed in the final forging. However, too low a finishing temperature will result in cracking and inadequate filling of the dies.

More generous fillets than usual are designed into magnesium forgings to reduce the danger of cracking at stress concentrators in the part during fabrication. The following conditions have been published as those under which magnesium frequently proves to be the most advantageous material to use for forgings: [1]

1. Applications where stiffness, strength in bending, or local instability are factors in the design of the parts.

2. Applications where the minimum forgeable section thickness does not allow full utilization of the strength of other metals.

3. Applications where dimensions of the part or the bosses, lugs, or flanges on the part, rather than the strength, are the important factor.

4. Applications where fatigue strength rather than static strength is the most important factor.

5. Applications requiring pressure tightness.

6. Applications requiring significant amount of machining.

7. Applications where a generally uniform quality throughout the part is essential.

Magnesium alloys are forged on presses of widely varying capacity, from 200 to 50,000 tons. Demands of the aircraft industry for large magnesium forgings have stimulated the use of larger and larger machines.

## 7.9   Preferred Orientation

The preferred orientations of magnesium alloy wrought products are of great importance in the control of the "directionality" of properties, material behavior in bending and drawing, and possibly even in their influence on chemical behavior of the magnesium alloys before a sharp preferred orientation is found. Only a few recrystallizations are necessary in magnesium alloys before a sharp preferred orientation is developed.

As can be seen in Tables 7.1 to 7.5, a lower compressive yield strength than tensile yield strength is the rule in magnesium alloy wrought products. The ratio of these two quantities approaches unity only in a few cases, particularly extruded ZK60A and AZ80A. In most of the products, the ratio lies between 0.5 and 0.7. Since the designer of lightweight structures is often more interested in the buckling properties which depend rather strongly on the compressive strength, this ratio is a rather important characteristic of the wrought magnesium product. It can be understood qualitatively in terms of the preferred orientation of these products.

Practically all the known rolling and extrusion textures of polycrystalline magnesium alloys can be systematized on the basis of their deviation from the "ideal" sheet or wire textures. The ideal sheet texture is defined as complete parallelism of the basal plane of all solid solution grains with the surface of the sheet or extruded flat. The ideal wire texture is defined in the same way except that the basal

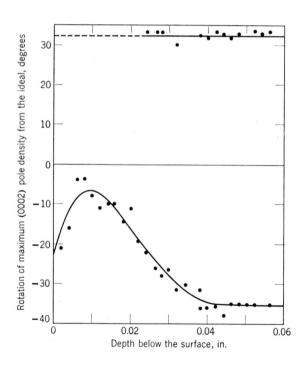

Fig. 7.13. Profile plot of preferred orientation peak rotation at different levels below the surface of a hot-extruded Mg-5.2% Th alloy flat of 0.125-in. thickness.[22] Positive rotation of basal pole toward the extrusion direction.

plane parallelism is only with the wire axis. The main deviations from the ideal are typed as follows:

1. Spread about the ideal as a center. This is very seldom observed.

2. Spread about a single-pole density peak, which is displaced from the ideal by rotation about the transverse direction.

3. A double peak, each of which is displaced from the ideal by rotation about the transverse direction.

4. A double peak, each of which is displaced from the ideal by rotation about the rolling or extrusion direction. This applies to sheet or flat extrusion only.

Different preferred orientations are encountered in magnesium alloys when one changes alloy composition, deformation conditions, or the level below the sheet or extrusion surface at which the measurements are made. The latter variation is much more important for extrusions than for sheet.

The characterization of the preferred orientation of a magnesium alloy sheet or extrusion by the use of one pole figure can be quite mis-

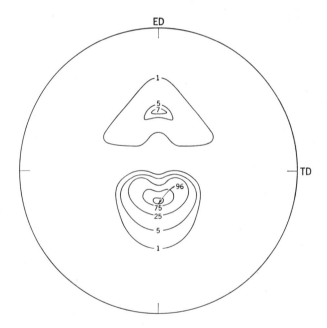

Fig. 7.14. (0002) pole figure for hot-extruded Mg-5.2% Th alloy taken at the surface of the 0.125-in. thick flat.[22] Contours represent relative x-ray diffraction intensities. ED—extrusion direction, TD—transverse direction.

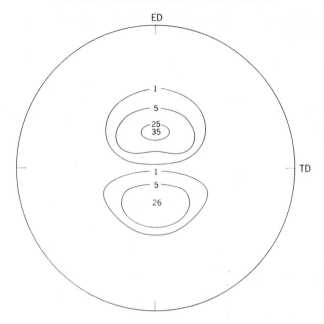

Fig. 7.15.  (0002) pole figure for hot-extruded Mg-5.2% Th alloy taken near the center of the 0.125-in. thick flat.[22]

leading.  The failure of most of the earlier investigators to examine variations of magnesium preferred orientation with depth reduces the general utility of their results.  The variation of the texture in rolled sheet or extrusions with depth below the surface is a direct result of the flow characteristics of polycrystalline magnesium.  This variation may be expressed by a series of pole figures taken at various depths in the metal or, more concisely but not as completely, by one or two pole figures at selected depths to show the texture types involved plus a plot of the variation of the peak pole density positions in rotation about some axis of the sheet or extrusion.  The latter will be called a *profile plot* here.  Except for the deviation which is described by (4) above, and which probably is the rarest, a profile plot about the transverse axis is a fairly good way of presenting the variation of preferred orientation with depth.

The most common sheet or flat extrusion texture in magnesium alloys is that with (3) the so-called double texture.[20, 21]  Two (0002) pole figures and a profile plot as determined by x-ray diffraction for an extruded Mg-5.2% Th alloy are presented in Figs. 7.13 to 7.15.

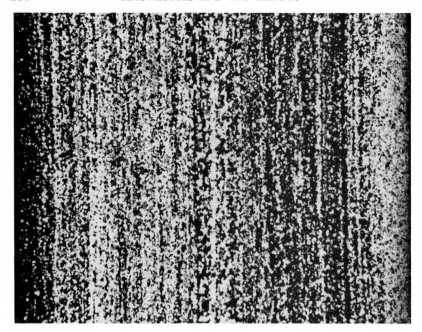

Fig. 7.16. "Short-range order" of preferred orientation in hot-extruded Mg-3.1% Th alloy.[23]  Cross section of 0.225-in. thick flat perpendicular to transverse direction.  Acetic picral etch.  Polarized light through orange filter.  (Dark grains appeared blue under polarized light and are of the negative peak of Fig. 7.17; light grains appeared orange and are of the positive peak.)  38.5×.

The minor or low density peak of the texture at the surface is shown by the dashed line in the profile plot.  Without measurement methods of high sensitivity, this element may be missed at the very surface, thus overlooking the double nature of the orientation.  This preferred orientation has been observed in the following magnesium alloys: [22]

Cold-rolled                     $Mg + 5.2\%$ Li
                                $Mg + 0.18\%$ Ca
                                $Mg + 1.5\%$ Mn
                                $Mg + 3\%$ Al $+ 1\%$ Zn $+ 0.02\%$ Ca
                                $Mg + 3\%$ Al $+ 1\%$ Zn $+ 0.14\%$ Ca

Hot-extruded electrolytic Mg
                                $Mg + 0.06\%$ Ce
                                $Mg + 0.7\%$ Ce
                                $Mg + 6.0\%$ Ce
                                $Mg + 3.4\%$ Th
                                $Mg + 5.2\%$ Th

Hot-extruded          Mg + 3.1% Th

                             Mg + 3% Th + 1% Mn

Cold-extruded        Mg + 3% Th + 1% Mn

The last three materials show a somewhat more pronounced minor element at the surface than the others.

The complete explanation of the development of preferred orientation is not yet possible. However, fortunately, experimental techniques have been developed and applied successfully to the study of inhomogeneities of the oriented aggregate. The use of an orientation-sensitive staining etch and polarized light allows the presentation of the "short-range order" of the double-peak texture for a hot-extruded Mg-3.1% Th alloy, Fig. 7.16.[23, 24] The dark and light grains corre-

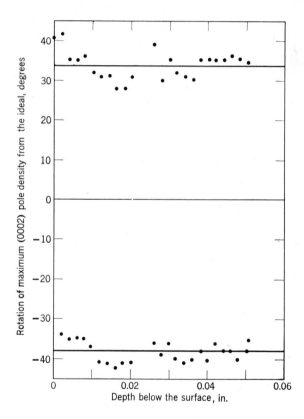

Fig. 7.17. Profile plot of preferred orientation peak rotation at different levels below the surface of a hot-extruded Mg-3.1% Th alloy flat with thickness of 0.125 in.[22] Positive rotation of basal plane pole toward the extrusion direction.

Fig. 7.18. Section of extrusion butt at die level from Mg-3.1% Th alloy. Acetic picral etched and photographed as in Fig. 7.16, 31✕. (Courtesy of S. L. Couling.)

spond to the two elements of the texture as shown in the profile plot of Fig. 7.17. They occur essentially in alternating layers parallel to the surface and of thickness varying from one to five of the recrystallized grain size. The configuration of recrystallized grains in the extrusion butt and die area is shown by the same orientation etch in Fig. 7.18. The superimposed lines show the basal plane inclination in the metal which becomes the major element of the texture at the extrusion surface. This metal flows from the part of the butt which is a transition between the "dead metal" in the upper left corner of the illustration and that part in the center which is flowing much more drastically. Detailed study of the grain structure and orientation has indicated that this surface material has flowed mainly under the influence of uniform shear resulting from the frictional drag of the die face.

The double texture may be explained by postulating primarily simple compression within the center of the flowing metal modified by an increasing shear component as the surface is approached. The influence of the shear component, which appears to be rather important in extrusion, but of little importance in rolling and negligible in compression, is to create a surface skin which contains a preponderance of one of the two band orientations.

There is a group of magnesium alloys in which the double rolling or extrusion texture is not always obtained. Prominent in this group are the Mg-Al binaries and the Mg-Al-Zn ternary alloys, the latter having great commercial importance. AZ31B when hot-rolled to 0.5-in. plate at about 260°C (500°F) shows the preferred orientation of type 1 above, as shown in Fig. 7.19. When 0.064-in. sheet is finished at about 120°C (250°F), type 2 is observed, as in Fig. 7.20. Cold-rolled AZ31B sheet sometimes shows the double-texture type 3. Hot extrusions of Mg-Al binaries show both types 1 and 2, depending upon the level below the surface. However, banding has been observed in some of these materials. The difference from the behavior of the double-peak texture group has not been explained.

The final preferred orientation, type 4, which involves rotation of material from the ideal orientation about the rolling or extrusion direction as an axis, has been observed in an extruded Mg + 4.6% Li alloy, Fig. 7.21. This is the same alloy in which large amounts of prismatic $\{10\bar{1}0\}$ $\langle 11\bar{2}0 \rangle$ slip were observed, as discussed in Section 4.2. It is in-

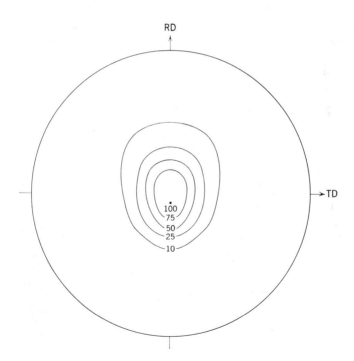

Fig. 7.19.  (0002) pole figure for hot-rolled AZ31B plate of 0.5-in. thickness.  RD—rolling direction.  TD—transverse direction.

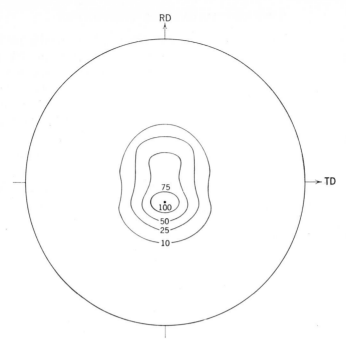

Fig. 7.20.   (0002) pole figure for warm-finished AZ31B sheet of 0.064-in. thickness.

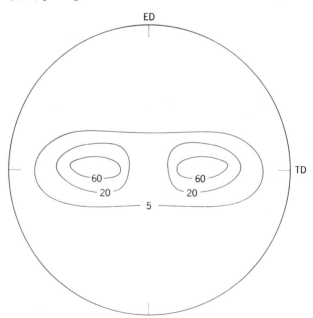

Fig. 7.21.   (0002) pole figure for hot-extruded Mg-4.6% Li alloy taken at surface.[25]

**190**

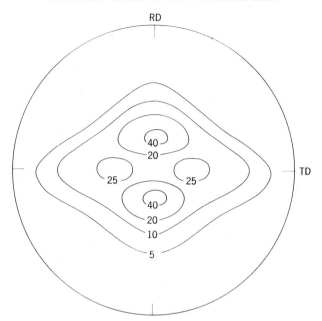

Fig. 7.22. (0002) pole figure for Mg-4.6% Li alloy, hot-extruded and cold-rolled to 70% reduction in thickness.[25]

teresting that the cold-rolling of this extrusion reorients material from the type 4 deviation back to type 3. A four-peak pole figure results, as shown by Pearsall,[25] Fig. 7.22.

The preferred orientation of a magnesium sheet, forging or extrusion is rather important in controlling its mechanical properties during further deformation, in bending or tension for example. Although complete explanations of this complex effect are not available, the following isolated observations have been made:

1. The more ideal the orientation, the better the tensile creep resistance of magnesium alloys, other things being equal.

2. A skin of narrow, near ideal orientation on the surface of rolled sheet is detrimental to ductility in bending.[26]

### References

1. *Magnesium Design,* The Dow Chemical Company, Midland, Mich., 1957.
2. *"Elektron" Magnesium Alloys Design,* Magnesium Elektron Limited, Clifton Junction, Manchester, England, 1956.

3. L. Sturkey (unpublished results), The Dow Chemical Company, Midland, Mich.

4. J. P. Doan and G. Ansel, "Some Effects of Zirconium on Extrusion Properties of Magnesium-Base Alloys Containing Zinc," *Trans. AIME,* **171,** 286 (1947).

5. J. C. McDonald, "Tensile Properties of Rolled Magnesium Alloys, I—Binary Alloys with Aluminum, Antimony, Bismuth, Cadmium, Copper, Lead, Nickel, Silver, Thallium, Tin and Zinc," *Trans. AIME,* **137,** 430 (1940).

6. P. T. Stroup, G. F. Sager, and J. B. West, "Magnesium Sheet," *Trans. ASM,* **35,** 195 (1944).

7. J. C. McDonald, "Tensile Properties of Rolled Magnesium Alloys—Binary Alloys with Calcium, Cerium, Gallium and Thorium," *Trans. AIME,* **143,** 179 (1941).

8. C. S. Roberts, "Creep Behavior of Magnesium-Cerium Alloys," *Trans. AIME,* **200,** 634 (1954).

9. T. E. Leontis, "New Magnesium Alloys for High Temperature," *Metal Progr.,* 97 (August 1957); also, "Uses of Thorium in Magnesium Technology," in *The Metal Thorium,* American Society for Metals, Cleveland, Ohio, 1958, pp. 29–56.

10. T. E. Leontis, "Effect of Rare-Earth Metals on the Properties of Extruded Magnesium," *Trans. AIME,* **191,** 987 (1951).

11. R. K. Paddock, "Direct Chill Continuous Casting of Magnesium Proves Practical, Economical," *Iron Age,* **274,** 249 (1954).

12. W. R. D. Jones and L. Powell, "The Rolling of a Magnesium Alloy," *J. Inst. Metals,* **67,** 153 (1941).

13. W. R. D. Jones, "The Effect of Rolling Temperature on the Mechanical Properties of a Magnesium Alloy," *J. Inst. Metals,* **70,** 149 (1944).

14. J. C. McDonald, "Anomalous Behavior During Cold Working and Subsequent Heating of Certain Magnesium Base Alloys," *Trans. AIME,* **212,** 45 (1958).

15. S. L. Couling, J. F. Pashak, and L. Sturkey, "Unique Deformation and Aging Characteristics of Certain Magnesium-Base Alloys," *Trans. ASM,* **51,** 94 (1959).

16. T. Ernst and F. Laves, "The Deformation of Magnesium and its Alloys," *Z. Metallk.,* **40,** 1 (1949).

17. S. L. Couling, "Yield Points in a Dilute Magnesium-Thorium Alloy," *Acta Met.* **7,** 133 (1959).

18. W. Schmidt, "Das Pressen von Stangen aus Elektrommetall," *Z. Metallk.,* **19,** 378 (1927).

19. R. S. Busk and T. E. Leontis, "The Extrusion of Powdered Magnesium Alloys," *Trans. AIME,* **188,** 297 (1950).

20. P. W. Bakarian, "Preferred Orientation in Rolled Magnesium and Magnesium Alloys," *Trans. AIME,* **147,** 266 (1942).

21. A. Hargreaves, "The Crystal Grain Orientation in a Rolled Magnesium Alloy," *J. Inst. Metals,* **71,** 73 (1945).

22. C. S. Roberts and E. C. Burke, "The Origin of the Double Peak in the Texture of Certain Rolled Magnesium Alloys," *Wright Air Development Center Tech. Rept.,* No. 55-160, Part 3 (1955).

23. S. L. Couling, "Investigation of Alloys of Magnesium and Their Properties," *Wright Air Development Center Tech. Rept.,* No. 57-194, Part 3 (1957).

24. S. L. Couling and G. W. Pearsall, "Determination of Orientation in Magnesium by Polarized Light Examination," *Trans. AIME,* **209,** 939 (1957).

25. G. W. Pearsall, discussion of "Deformation and Fracture of Alpha Solid Solutions of Lithium in Magnesium," F. E. Hauser, P. R. Landon and J. E. Dorn, *Trans. ASM,* **50,** 856 (1958).

26. R. L. Dietrich, "Surface Orientation and Rolling of Magnesium Sheet," *Trans. AIME,* **185,** 621 (1949).

27. W. Rosenkranz, "Das Schmieden und Gesenkpressen von Magnesiumlegierungen von Mg-Al-Zn Typ," *Z. Metallk.,* **47,** 107 (1956).

28. G. Ansel and J. O. Betterton, Jr., "The Hot and Cold Rolling of Magnesium-Base Alloys," *Trans. AIME,* **171** (1947).

29. *Magnesium—Fabricating and Casting,* Organization for European Economic Cooperation, Paris, 1956.

30. G. Sachs and K. R. Van Horn, *Practical Metallurgy,* American Society for Metals, Cleveland, Ohio, 1940.

31. C. E. Pearson, *The Extrusion of Metals,* John Wiley & Sons, New York, 1944.

# 8

# Chemical
# Properties
# and
# Applications

## 8.1 Anodic Behavior of Magnesium

The pronounced reactivity of the metal is expressed clearly by its position in the electrochemical series, its standard electrode potential versus hydrogen being $-2.40$ v which is only 0.3 v noble to sodium. In most aqueous electrolytes, the equilibrium potential of the magnesium electrode is more noble (less electronegative) than its standard electrode potential, due to polarization and film formation, and it is this film formation that enables magnesium and its alloys to withstand aqueous environments without the rapid and complete dissolution suffered by sodium.[1-8] The films formed in aqueous exposure are usually composed predominantly of hexagonal $Mg(OH)_2$. However, basic salt formation, particularly involving the basic halides, has been observed in the corrosion of zinc, and the possibility of such behavior for magnesium corrosion should not be ignored.

It may be predicted from the reactivity of magnesium with water that the electrolysis of metallic magnesium from aqueous solutions is not possible. It is found in practice that only hydrogen evolution at the cathode results if such an electrolysis is attempted.

Magnesium hydroxide is more strongly basic than the hydrous oxides of the other light structural metals. For example, the hydrous oxides of aluminum are poorly soluble over the $pH$ range of about 4 to 9. They are also generally protective in this region, whereas magnesium hydroxide does not become poorly soluble and thus protective until the $pH$ exceeds 10. However, since magnesium hydroxide is not amphoteric, the protection is maintained throughout the alkaline region. In addition to its ability to resist alkaline solutions, magnesium also resists hydrofluoric acid and its salts through the formation of protective films of mixed magnesium hydroxide and magnesium fluoride.[6]

In view of the extremely active potential of magnesium, it is not surprising that its corrosion in aqueous electrolytes occurs predominantly by hydrogen evolution. However, in the presence of oxygen, and if the electrolyte is present as a thin film or if exposure is made to distilled water, oxygen reduction may become important to the corrosion process. Both of these exposure conditions increase the electrical resistance of the electrolytic path for the local corrosion and thus permit the local cathode to operate at the more passive potentials characteristic of the oxygen reduction process. In addition, the diffusion of oxygen to the metal surface occurs much more rapidly through a film of electrolyte than it does through the same electrolyte in bulk. It is interesting to note that increasing the rate of oxygen supply by increasing its partial pressure over the electrolyte results in *both* increased oxygen reduction and hydrogen evolution. This result is a consequence of the "negative difference effect," which will be referred to again in Section 8.3.

## 8.2   Corrosion of Magnesium Alloys

It had been found in the earliest days of magnesium alloy development that intentional alloying elements and heat treatments could have marked influence on the corrosion rate in specified environments. However, no reasonably simple understanding of the trends and the scatter of available corrosion data were possible until the completion of the work of Hanawalt et al. on the effect of minor level impurities on the corrosion of magnesium.[9] Corrosion proceeds most rapidly when many local cells are available with magnesium as the anode and another phase as the cathode. Three impurities—iron, nickel, and copper—are common to magnesium and are also extremely effective microscopic cathodes. Hanawalt et al. found that the amount of these impurities was the factor of primary importance in determining the corrosion rate of magnesium and its alloys in sodium chloride solution. They found that in "pure" magnesium, the corrosion rate increased rapidly as the content of iron, copper, and nickel was increased beyond 170, 1300, and 5 ppm respectively. Later work has shown that the degree of dispersion of the iron particles in particular, i.e., the number of them, is important also in controlling the corrosion rate. However, the specification of "tolerance limits" for these three impurities, as they were called by the pioneer investigators, continues to be an important technological control of the corrosion resistance of magnesium alloys.

A quantitative development of the corrosion-rate—impurity-content dependence was published by Bushrod.[10] Although he offers some cogent criticisms of the basic theory put forward by Hanawalt et al., a better fundamental explanation of the impurity effect has not been proposed since.

Copper and nickel content of magnesium alloys can be controlled rather well with careful monitoring of scrap additions in melting and by the specification of low nickel content in the alloys from which melting equipment is fabricated, as was mentioned in Section 6.7. The greatest attention in the melting operations must be given to control of iron content since the magnesium is handled in iron alloy containers, both at the primary metal production step and in melting and alloying for the foundry or the mill. Intentional alloying elements in magnesium can influence the corrosion behavior in several ways:

1. Alloying elements in general reduce the electrode activity from that of pure magnesium. The corrosion rate may be expected to decrease accordingly.

2. The tolerance limit for the damaging impurities may be changed. Aluminum was found to decrease the tolerance limit for iron to less than 2 ppm at the 10% level.

3. The corrosion rate may be reduced when the tolerance limit has been exceeded. Manganese and zinc are the two most important alloying elements in this respect. They both reduce the corrosion rate when added to magnesium and Mg-Al alloys containing appreciable amounts of iron.

The effect of manganese in the technology is probably twofold. It lowers the iron content of the melt before casting the metal and it tends to surround iron particles during freezing, thus rendering them inactive as cathodes in the final alloy.[11,12] The iron-settling effect of zirconium allows good corrosion resistance in the large group of newer alloys which contain this element. Manganese is an especially important alloying element from the standpoint of corrosion resistance in the Mg-Al alloy series.

Processing impurities, such as rolling scale, can also have marked effect on the corrosion of magnesium alloys. The corrosion rate of rolled sheet in NaCl solution can be reduced by as large a factor as 100 by pickling off such contaminants.

The most severely corrosive environments for magnesium alloys are dilute chloride solutions and dilute acids, particularly the mineral acids and those of the organic complexing group, such as acetic and tartaric. Immersion in approximately 3% NaCl solution is a common test for corrosion resistance which shows the magnesium alloys at their worst. Corrosion rate in NaCl solution has little relation to corrosion rate in other environments. The continual use of NaCl testing leads to unrealistic results if and when the metal is to be used in a salt-free environment, which is often the case. The reproducibility of corrosion rate is generally poor with salt solutions, but good with acid in Whitby's results,[13,14] probably because of diffusion control in the latter.[3] The film-damaging effect of the chloride ion may be essentially smothered by bulk formation of a heavy hydroxide layer, according to Loose and Uhlig.[15] They report that the addition of 48% NaOH to a 4% NaCl solution reduces the corrosion rate from 15–30 mg/dm$^2$/day (mdd) to 1–2 mdd. Van Muylder and Pourbaix show that $CO_2$ and $H_3PO_4$ may be expected to impede corrosion, and they state that vanadates and chromates accomplish the same purpose, namely, the formation of protective films which passivate the surface.[1]

The relatively high corrosion resistance of magnesium alloys of controlled purity (1–100 mdd in various environments) argues that the protective film, which is maintainable in alloys of lower impurity contents than the "tolerance limits," has a high hydrogen overvoltage. This is probably a natural consequence of the good electrical insulating properties of $Mg(OH)_2$.

The importance of the impurity content and the interaction between impurity effects and the alloying elements decrease as magnesium alloys are corroded in lower conductivity environments. The resistance of all the magnesium alloys to rural and urban weathering is generally adequate, judging from Holler and Frye's ratings.[16] In all of these environments, bare magnesium rapidly becomes covered with a uniform film which varies from light to dark gray.

Whitby found that in indoor atmosphere the corrosion rate is controlled by the relative humidity.[17] The primary reaction was formation of $Mg(OH)_2$, but he found that this film normally became protective by secondary reactions. These are the formation of hydrated carbonates and sulfates so that the film is usually a mixture of these with the hydroxide. The proportion of sulfate increases in *outdoor* exposure with the carbonate still predominant. He observed that the corrosion film always loses weight after rain because of the solution of sulfates. During dry periods, the film thickens again.

The severely damaging effect of the chloride ion on the protective film is the reason for the great concern for the prevention of flux inclusion in casting magnesium, as was discussed in Chapter 6. In addition to containing the chloride ion, almost all of the common magnesium melting fluxes are hygroscopic, thus fostering corrosion even in a relatively dry environment.

The phenomenon of galvanic corrosion, which involves the undesired formation of a gross electrolytic couple between magnesium and another metal, is discussed at the end of the next section.

Magnesium and its alloys exhibit some stress corrosion, with cracking primarily through the grains and secondarily along the boundaries. Sensitivity is greater in wrought products than in castings. Aluminum-rich wrought alloys, such as AZ61A, have higher stress corrosion sensitivity than the Mg-Mn and Mg-Zn-Zr alloys. The thorium alloys generally have low sensitivity; HK31A is substantially insensitive. The mechanism of stress corrosion in magnesium alloys is the subject of considerable theoretical controversy and conflicting experimental data. Contributions have been made by Heidenreich et al.,[18] Perryman,[19] and Priest et al.[20]

The elevated temperature oxidation of magnesium has been studied by Leontis and Rhines.[21] A protective continuous film of the oxide forms below 450°C in dry air or oxygen. This film appears to lose its mechanical integrity above 450°C, thus offering comparatively little protection. Linear oxidation rates were observed. Alloying increased oxidation rates whenever the melting point was significantly decreased.

The difference between dry and moist oxygen as the oxidant for magnesium has been studied by Gregg and Jepson.[22] They used five different surface preparation methods and studied the oxidation over the range 350–600°C. Weight-gain curves are characterized by an induction period followed by a linear branch. In agreement with Leontis and Rhines, a second linear branch is found above 525°C when dry oxygen is used. Moisture lowers the temperature at which the oxide is no longer protective. It also shortens the induction period, increases the linear oxidation rate, and interferes with the second linear branch of the process. It is thought that moisture promotes the oxidation rate by the incorporation of hydroxyl ions in the oxide film.

The reaction between magnesium and water vapor between 31 and 208 mm Hg pressure and between 425° and 575° has been investigated by Svec and Gibbs.[23]   The rate constant is a linear function of water vapor pressure.   In the middle of the temperature range studied, the reaction appears to shift from the surface to the gas phase because of increasing magnesium vapor pressure.

## 8.3    Protective Anodes

Magnesium, with its very active electrode potential will protect most of the other common structural metals from corrosion when it is connected in a closed electric circuit with them.   The magnesium acts as the anode in the circuit and is consumed sacrificially to protect the more noble metal, which acts as the cathode.   The most important application of cathodic protection at present is in the protection of large steel structures, either underground, as in the case of pipelines and storage tanks or in liquids, such as water heaters and steel ships. Both aluminum and zinc have been used in this application since they are both anodic to iron.   The familiar zinc-plated steel gains its corrosion resistance from the sacrificial characteristic of the zinc coating. Large- as well as small-scale applications of rectifier-produced direct current have been used in corrosion prevention for several years. However, the greatest strides have been made by the magnesium alloy anode because of the high cell voltage, the inherently low electrical equivalent weight, and the continual improvement of the current efficiency resulting from product development.   The current efficiency is the ratio of the charge transferred through the external circuit and, therefore, is effective in protecting the cathode structure to the charge corresponding to the equivalent weight of anode alloy dissolved.   Loss in anode current efficiency from the ideal value of 100% is thought to result primarily from the occurrence of local corrosion on the surface of the anode, thereby "short-circuiting" the protective circuit. One might expect that at high current drains in the protective circuit, the efficiency might approach 100% because of a relative constancy of the local corrosion losses.

The efficiency does increase markedly as a function of drain.   However, it approaches a value $< 100\%$ as a limit.   This is known as the "negative difference effect," which is explained in terms of the damage to the protective film on the anode with increasing current drain.   The behavior is well described by the relation $W_i = W_0 + (100/E)nFit$, where $W_i$ is the loss of weight of the anode at current $i$ and time $t, W_0$ is the open-circuit weight loss for a similar time, $F$ is the Faraday constant, and $n$ is the ion valence.   The anode efficiency is then:

$$\% \ E \ = \ \frac{nFit}{W_0 \ + \ (100/E') \ nFit}$$

and $\lim_{i \to \infty} \% \ E \ = \ E'$. $E'$ is generally between 60% and 70% in aqueous environments. However, it has been known to exceed 90% in strongly inhibited systems and, in a few cases, it has been found to be less than 50%.

It has also been suggested by Petty et al.[24] and Greenblatt [25] that the cause of this increase in corrosion with anodic drain is the production of transitory monovalent magnesium ions as well as the expected divalent ions. It is interesting to note, however, that in nonaqueous solutions which lack electron acceptors the current yield is quantitative based on the divalent process. However, if electron-accepting molecules are then added to the electrolyte, the current yield is decreased, according to Rausch et al.[26] The presence of an electron acceptor in the electrolyte is a necessary condition for local corrosion.

The practice in the protection of underground structures is the burial of cast anodes of magnesium alloy in a hole surrounded by backfill, a mixture of chemicals, usually gypsum and bentonite, at a level and distance from the structure which will allow maximum safely protected area for that anode. A connecting cable is then run to the structure and the hole and the cable ditch is filled. The purpose of the backfill is:

1. To reduce the anode-to-earth resistance and thus to enable delivery of more current per unit of installation.

2. To stabilize the anode potential by preventing polarization.

3. To improve the anode efficiency by reducing parasitic corrosion.

4. To bring about a more uniform pattern of corrosion attack at the anode.

The practice in ship hull installation is to bolt the magnesium alloy ingot directly to the steel plate.

A thorough series of alloy studies have been made on the protective anode. Robinson and Osborn [27-29] summarized the results. The Mg- 6%Al- 3%Zn alloy corresponding roughly to the casting alloy AZ63 has been proved the best of many binary and ternary alloys. It is once again important to hold the iron, copper, and nickel content of the alloy low to achieve good anode efficiencies. The authors found that at a current flow equivalent to ten years of life, an efficiency of 50–60%, corresponding to between 500 and 600 amp-hr/lb, is obtained except in high-chloride soils, where higher current densities are needed to get comparable efficiencies. Although they found that occasionally outstanding current efficiencies were obtained from an unalloyed magnesium anode, in general, the high-purity AZ63 alloy was the best under varied conditions of application. A later report by Robinson and George [12] emphasized the need for high purity, and identified lead and tin as detrimental impurities to the anode efficiency *in addition* to those elements cited above. As in the case of general corrosion resistance, manganese was found to be very useful in controlling the deleterious effects of iron and perhaps copper. The efficient behavior of the alloy was found not to be sensitive to the aluminum and zinc content or to small additions of beryllium.

The establishment of a large-area galvanic cell with magnesium as the anode and another metal or alloy as the cathode is also the basis of the detrimental effect of galvanic corrosion at contacts between dissimilar metals in environments where any appreciable amount of moisture exists. Since magnesium is anodic to practically all structural metals and alloys, it is necessary to produce a satisfactory amount of corrosion resistance by carefully choosing the alloys with which the magnesium alloy will come in contact. It has been found that aluminum-based alloys which are rich in magnesium, e.g., 5056, 5052, 6061, and 6053, generally cause only slight galvanic corrosion to magnesium. The copper-rich aluminum-based alloys, such as 2014, 2017, and 2024, cause more severe galvanic corrosion. Tin, zinc, and cadmium cause only moderate galvanic corrosion to magnesium alloys and thus are extensively used as electrodeposits on iron-, copper-, and nickel-rich alloys which can cause very severe galvanic corrosion to the magnesium if the environment is strongly electrolytic.[30]

Research efforts in The Dow Chemical Company have shown that high-purity aluminum is extremely compatible with magnesium.[31] Very little galvanic corrosion is observed either on the magnesium or on the aluminum member of the couple when magnesium is coupled to 99.99%+ purity aluminum. It was concluded that the compatibility of an aluminum alloy when coupled to a magnesium alloy is determined primarily by:

1. *The heavy metal content of the aluminum alloy.* Iron, copper and nickel, in particular, are extremely deleterious and must be controlled at low levels for complete compatibility. As the heavy metal content increases, the compatibility decreases.

2. *The magnesium content of the aluminum alloy.* Increasing the magnesium content causes partial or, in some cases, complete suppression of the effects of iron, copper, and nickel.

3. *The environment of the couple.* Sea water has a far less corrosive effect than does unbuffered NaCl solution.

4. *The solution potential of the magnesium alloy.* The thorium-containing alloys, in particular HK31A alloy, have more electronegative potentials than do the Al-Zn alloys such as AZ31B. Thus, some aluminum alloys which are extremely compatible with AZ31B are somewhat less compatible with HK31A.

A shear strength evaluation of both high-purity and commercial-purity aluminum alloys (5052, 5056, and 6061 types) indicated excellent possibilities for the development of a satisfactory fastener for magnesium alloys for both room- and elevated-temperature service. Unexpectedly high shear strengths obtained for 5056 aluminum enhance its position as a rivet alloy for this service. A reduction of heavy metal impurities in this alloy also results in a high degree of galvanic compatibility with magnesium. This compatibility does not suffer on prolonged elevated-temperature aging.

The results suggested another valuable application. An electrode-posited aluminum coating on steel fasteners produces a hardware item which displays excellent galvanic compatibility with magnesium alloys.

It has also been established that galvanic corrosion can occur between various magnesium alloys.[32] Such corrosion is not generally serious.

## 8.4   The Magnesium Dry Cell

The extremely low equivalent weight of magnesium (12.16 as compared with 32.7 for zinc) combined with its more active anode potential has made magnesium attractive for the dry-cell field for a long time. It has already made a place in the manufacture of a specialty type—the reserve battery—which is assembled in a much drier state than the usual dry cell. The shelf life is almost infinite until the reserve cell is activated by immersion in water, after which it must be used rather rapidly. Primary applications are in the military field where the active potentials and light weight of magnesium anodes supplement the basic weight saving of the reserve-cell principle. Two types have been found commercially useful for reserve applications: the silver chloride-magnesium cell, as described by Blake,[33] and the cuprous chloride-magnesium cell, as reported by Pucher.[34] In the former, an anode of unalloyed magnesium and a cathode system of silver and silver chloride are separated by an absorbent sheet of cellulosic material. The reactions are:

$$Mg \rightleftharpoons Mg^{++} + 2e^-$$

$$2AgCl + 2e^- \rightleftharpoons 2Cl^- + 2Ag$$

$$Mg^{++} + 2Cl^- \rightleftharpoons MgCl_2 \cdot 6H_2O$$

They proceed very rapidly, bringing the cell to its full voltage and current in a few minutes. The voltage ranges from 1.3 to 1.6 v per cell. When the AgCl is completely reduced, the cell voltage falls rapidly. These cells offer the advantages of high current and power output, constant potential, light weight, long shelf life, and satisfactory discharge at temperatures from $+94°C$ to $-54°C$. The silver content renders them rather expensive.

The cuprous chloride reserve cell is constructed from a sheet of commercially pure magnesium separated from the cuprous chloride cathode by porous synthetic fiber. When the cell is wet, the open-circuit voltage builds up rapidly to 1.7–1.8 v at $22°C$. The reactions are equivalent to those in the silver chloride cell except for the substitution of copper for silver. This cell is cheaper to manufacture than the silver chloride cell, but has somewhat less output power per unit weight. In the other advantageous respects listed above they are very similar.

Much effort has been expended on the development of a magnesium dry cell. The Dow Chemical Company has succeeded in developing such cells to the point that they are now being seriously considered for military as well as commercial applications. The Dow development resulted in a very-high-capacity cell, particularly when the load resistance is designed to match the higher voltage level as compared with the conventional zinc cell. The most suitable anode alloy is AZ31A (basically Mg- 3%Al- 1%Zn- 0.2%Mn- 0.15%Ca), according to Kirk et al.[35] The calcium appears to aid in reducing the "delay time," an anode turn-on polarization phenomenon that has dropped from tens to fractions of seconds as a result of the intensive development program which has been carried out for this cell. The cathode is made from $MnO_2 + BaCrO_4$ + acetylene black. A typical electrolyte is magnesium bromide inhibited with zinc chromate. A paper separator is used. In series battery applications, a marked advantage over zinc results from the higher output voltage per cell. Between 15 and 30% fewer cells are required for a given series cell voltage.

The anode efficiency is about 60%, as in the case of the protective anode. Although this compares poorly with the 90% or greater obtained with zinc, less magnesium is still consumed in the cell discharge because of the very favorable equivalent weight ratio. The magnesium cells have shown good low-temperature discharge properties and also have good storage characteristics.

## 8.5   Important Chemical Applications

The use of magnesium alloy as photoengraving plate has been one of the most promising developments in the chemical marketing of magnesium. PE alloy (basically AZ31 with an especially low manganese content), in sheet form, has been combined with the development of a new "rapid etch" process to give the photoengraving industry the benefit of a more economical production of high-quality engraving. The rapid-etch process, as developed by The Dow Chemical Company, involves the use of a complex etching bath of mixed acids and other addition agents. The magnesium alloy surface, which has previously been photographically prepared with acid-resistant masking material, is sprayed with the bath in a specially designed machine. The peculiar combination of the etching characteristics of magnesium and the composition of the bath allow the production of a deep etch of either line work, halftone, or type face without undercutting in one step of a few minutes duration. The traditional method of etching to the proper depth in zinc prior to this development involved the use of various protective agents which were made to adhere to the side of the etched pattern to avoid undercutting. The etching operations comprised several successive stages of attack and protection. The image quality which has been obtained with magnesium and the new process is a distinct improvement over that from previous materials and methods. As a result, the photoengraving of entire pages of newspapers has been found worth while. The need for roller plates is easily accomplished either by the bending of thin magnesium sheet into the proper holding form or by the use of extruded tubing of the proper diameter as the starting material.

One of the largest consumptions of magnesium in the United States is in the alloying to other metals. Practically all of this is going into aluminum-based alloys, where magnesium is an important alloying element that confers improved corrosion resistance as well as increased strength.

Another large use of magnesium is in the reduction or other processing of various metals. The largest single use in this category is in the titanium industry, where magnesium is one of the reducing agents in the tetrachloride process. Magnesium is also a useful inoculant in the production of nodular cast iron.

The traditional applications of magnesium in pyrotechnics have continued and have been supplemented by some interest in finely divided particles of the metal as a fuel in special applications. The systematization of the atomizing process in the Dow laboratories has helped to foster such special uses of finely divided magnesium.

Magnesium has had a traditional place in the field of organic chemistry ever since the discovery of the Grignard reactions in 1900. In this almost unlimited group of processes, magnesium is bound into compounds of the type RMgX, where R is an organic radical and X is chlorine, bromine, or iodine. Such organomagnesium compounds are primarily important as intermediates in the conversion of aldehydes and ketones to alcohols, for example. Although several organometallic compounds may be formed, the Grignard reagents are the most important commercially because of the ease with which magnesium reacts with organic halides and other compounds to form organomagnesium compounds, and because of the great versatility of these compounds as intermediates in difficult reactions. It appears that, although much investigation has been directed to the full understanding of the many reactions in which they participate, relatively little has been devoted to the understanding of why magnesium is so effective in this compound formation.

# References

1. J. Van Muylder and M. Pourbaix, "Electrochemical Behavior of Magnesium, $p$H-Voltage Equilibrium Diagrams of Systems $Mg-H_2O$, $Mg-CO_2-H_2O$ and $Mg-H_3PO_4-H_2O$ at 25°C," *Centre belge étude corrosion, Tech. Rept. No. 39,* March 1956.

2. W. M. Latimer, *Oxidation Potentials,* Prentice-Hall, Englewood Cliffs, N. J., 1938, 272.

3. C. V. King and W. H. Cathcart, "The Rate of Dissolution of Magnesium in Acids," *J. Am. Chem. Soc.,* **59,** 63 (1937).

4. G. Baborovsky, "Über das Verhalten von Magnesium Anoden," *Z. Elektrochem.,* **11,** 465 (1905).

5. S. Bodforss, "Zur Elektrochemie des Magnesiums," *Z. physik. Chem.,* **A153,** 83 (1931).

6. S. Yamaguchi, "Protective Films on Magnesium Observed by Electron Diffraction and Microscopy," *J. Appl. Phys.,* **25,** 1437 (1954).

7. E. S. Freeman and S. Gordon, "The Kinetics of the Underwater Corrosion of Powdered Magnesium," *J. Phys. Chem.,* **59,** 1009 (1955).

8. K. Huber, "Anodic Formation of Coatings on Magnesium, Zinc and Cadmium," *J. Electrochem. Soc.*, **100**, 376 (1953).

9. J. D. Hanawalt, C. E. Nelson, and J. A. Peloubet, "Corrosion Studies of Magnesium and its Alloys," *Trans. AIME*, **147**, 273 (1942).

10. C. J. Bushrod, "Note on the Quantitative Implications of Hanawalt's Theory of Corrosion of Magnesium-Base Alloys," *J. Inst. Metals*, **73**, 567 (1947)

11. C. E. Nelson, "The Melting and Refining of Magnesium," *Trans. AIME*, **159**, 392 (1944).

12. H. A. Robinson and P. F. George, "Effect of Alloying and Impurity Elements in Magnesium Alloy Cast Anodes," *Corrosion*, **10**, 182 (1954).

13. L. Whitby, "The Dissolution of Magnesium in Aqueous Salt Solutions, Part I," *Trans. Faraday Soc.*, **29**, 415 (1933).

14. L. Whitby, "The Dissolution of Magnesium in Aqueous Salt Solutions, Part II," *Trans. Faraday Soc.*, **29**, 853 (1933).

15. W. S. Loose, "Magnesium and Magnesium Alloys" in *Corrosion Handbook* (H. H. Uhlig, Ed.), John Wiley & Sons, New York, 1948, p. 223.

16. H. D. Holler and R. A. Frye, "Corrosion Ratings for Metals," *Corrosion*, **3**, 8 (1947).

17. L. Whitby, "The Atmospheric Corrosion of Magnesium," *Trans. Faraday Soc.*, **29**, 844 (1933).

18. R. D. Heidenreich, C. H. Gerould, and R. F. McNulty, "Electron Metallographic Methods and Some Results for Magnesium Alloys," *Trans. AIME*, **166**, 15 (1946).

19. E. C. W. Perryman, "Stress-Corrosion of Magnesium Alloys," *J. Inst. Metals*, **78**, 621 (1951).

20. D. K. Priest, F. H. Beck, and M. G. Fontana, "Stress-Corrosion Mechanism in a Magnesium-Base Alloy," *Trans. ASM*, **47**, 473 (1955).

21. T. E. Leontis and F. N. Rhines, "Rates of High-Temperature Oxidation of Magnesium and Magnesium Alloys," *Trans. AIME*, **166**, 265 (1946).

22. S. J. Gregg and W. B. Jepson, "The High Temperature Oxidation of Magnesium in Dry and Moist Oxygen," *J. Inst. Metals*, **87**, 187 (1959).

23. H. J. Svec and D. S. Gibbs, "Metal-Water Reactions. V—Kinetics of the Reaction Between Magnesium and Water Vapor," *J. Electrochem. Soc.*, **104**, 434 (1957).

24. R. L. Petty, A. W. Davidson, and J. Kleinberg, "The Anodic Oxidation of Magnesium Metal. Evidence for the Existence of Unipositive Magnesium," *J. Am. Chem. Soc.*, **76**, 363 (1954).

25. J. H. Greenblatt, "A Mechanism for the Anodic Dissolution of Magnesium," *J. Electrochem. Soc.*, **103**, 539 (1956).

26. M. D. Rausch, W. E. McEwen, and J. Kleinberg, "Reductions Involving Unipositive Magnesium," *Chem. Revs.*, **57**, 417 (1957).

27. H. A. Robinson, "Magnesium Anodes for the Cathodic Protection of Underground Structures," *Corrosion*, **2**, 199 (1946).

28. H. A. Robinson, "Magnesium As A Galvanic Anode. Some Factors Affecting Its Performance," *Trans. Electrochem. Soc.*, **90**, 485 (1946).

29. O. Osborn and H. A. Robinson, "Performance of Magnesium Galvanic Anodes in Underground Service," *Corrosion*, **8**, 114 (1952).

30. K. G. Compton, A. Mendizza, and W. W. Bradley, "Atmospheric Galvanic Couple Corrosion," *Corrosion*, **11**, 383t–392t (1955).

31. J. L. Nichols, "Progress Report—Aluminum Fasteners for Magnesium," The Dow Chemical Company, Midland, Mich., 1958.
32. F. A. Fox and J. K. Davies, "The Corrosion of Some Magnesium-Base Alloys (High and Normal Purity) in Contact with Other Metals," *J. Inst. Metals,* **73,** 553 (1947).
33. I. C. Blake, "Silver Chloride Magnesium Reserve Battery," *J. Electrochem. Soc.,* **99,** 202c (1952).
34. L. E. Pucher, "The Cuprous Chloride-Magnesium Reserve Battery," *J. Electrochem. Soc.,* **99,** 203c (1952).
35. R. C. Kirk, P. F. George, and A. B. Fry, "High Capacity Magnesium Dry Cells," *J. Electrochem. Soc.,* **99,** 323 (1952).

# 9

## The Extraction
## and Refining
## of Magnesium

### 9.1 Raw Material Sources

The extractive metallurgy of magnesium is intriguing because of
the diversity of processes which have competed at different times in
the history of the metal and in so many different parts of the world.
Complete descriptions of the details and the historical aspect of magnesium extraction appear in many places.[1-5] Here it seems appropriate to discuss briefly only those processes that have been used recently
or are being used now with commercial success.

Just as in the case of other metals, the development of magnesium
from the curiosity or rare metal stage to where it plays a significant
part in the world's economy depended on the development of satisfactory processes for extracting the metal from the raw materials of
nature. An extraction process must be satisfactory from two stand-
points; it must be economical and it must produce metal of adequate
purity to allow useful applications.

Magnesium is the sixth most common metal and the eighth most
common element in the earth's surface. It exists both in mineral deposits and in aqueous solutions. The most common minerals are the
carbonates, dolomite, $MgCO_3 \cdot CaCO_3$, and magnesite, $MgCO_3$. The
oxide mineral brucite, $MgO \cdot H_2O$, is somewhat rarer, as are the chlor-
ides, of which carnallite, $MgCl_2 \cdot KCl \cdot 6H_2O$, has been exploited the
most. Concentrated aqueous solutions in the form of brine deposits
occur at several places in the world, but by far the largest solution
deposit is the water of the world's oceans. The magnesium content
of the ocean (0.13%) is lower than that of even the lowest grade deposits of the minerals referred to above. Nevertheless, sea water has

two great advantages that have made it the primary source of the metal today. First, it may be mined at an economically favorable location and, second, it offers extreme uniformity of magnesium content, thus allowing easier standardization of the process.

All the processes which have been used since the earliest work of the Germans before the turn of the twentieth century may be grouped into two classes—electrolytic and direct reduction. Ever since the pioneer work of Faraday in 1833 and Bunsen in 1852, the most successful electrolytic processes have employed molten magnesium chloride in various degrees of dehydration. Some processes have used the oxide in a fluoride bath, as is practiced in the extractive metallurgy of aluminum, but these have not been able to compete with the chloride processes. The direct reduction processes have been carried out with the aid of silicon and carbon as the reducing agents. When electric power can be generated at a low cost, the electrolytic reduction processes have a definite economic advantage and they have become the principal method of winning the metal from the earth. The direct reduction processes once offered the advantage of producing purer metal, but improvements in the electrolytic process have now eliminated it. The direct reduction processes are often economically marginal in areas where power costs are low, and have been used to a great extent only in wartime emergency.

## 9.2    The Electrolytic Reduction Processes

The two general methods that fall into this group have accounted for the greatest amount of magnesium produced by man. The first was pioneered by the German firm of I.G. Farbenindustrie during the first 30 years of this century, and was later practiced extensively by the British firm, Magnesium Elektron Ltd. After breaking its German ties as a result of World War II, M.E.L. became the leading manufacturer of magnesium alloys in postwar Europe. The second process was developed by Dr. Herbert Dow of The Dow Chemical Company in the United States. His early work in the years of 1910–1920 and his continuing faith in the metal from that time to his death launched his company into the leading position that it now holds in the magnesium industry.

Both processes employ magnesium chloride as the cell feed. They differ only in the degree of dehydration of the chloride and the characteristics of the cell. Although the differences are important eco-

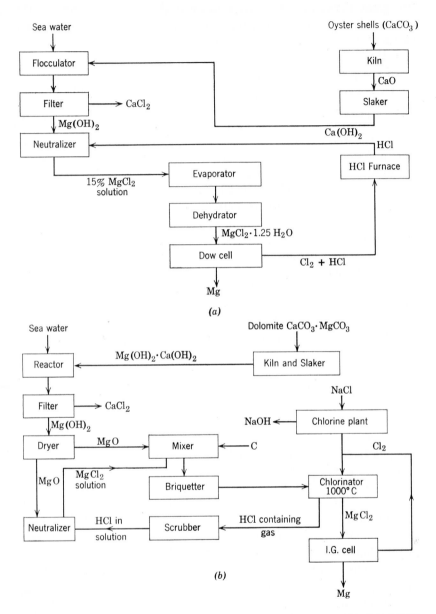

Fig. 9.1.   Electrolytic reduction processes.   (a) Dow process;  (b) I.G.-M.E.L. process.

Table 9.1.    Contrast of the Principal Electrolytic
Reduction Processes

| Dow Process | I.G. Process |
|---|---|
| 1. $MgCl_2 \cdot 1.25\ H_2O$ cell feed | 1. Anhydrous $MgCl_2$ cell feed |
| 2. Steel pot | 2. Refractory lined cell |
| 3. External heating of cell | 3. No external heat |
| 4. Replaceable carbon rod anodes | 4. Fixed carbon plate anodes |
| 5. Anode consumption about 0.1 lb/lb Mg from contained water | 5. Anode consumption about 0.015 lb/lb Mg |
| 6. Pot is cathode | 6. Cast-steel cathodes |
| 7. 30–70,000 amp | 7. 20,000 amp |
| 8. Magnesium ladled from collecting chamber may be cast directly as ingot or used for alloying | 8. Magnesium ladled from collecting chamber must be cleaned before casting, in general |
| 9. 8.5 kw-hr/lb Mg | 9. 8.5–9 kw-hr/lb Mg |

nomically, from a chemical standpoint the processes are not greatly different. The simple flow sheets of each process are shown in Fig. 9.1, and Table 9.1 summarizes the differences which are not readily apparent from the figure. It can be seen that some of the differences lead to economic operational advantages for one process or the other. Both processes have been adapted to the use of sea water, as the figure shows. Although claims to the pioneer work in this respect have been made by M.E.L., the great economic advantage of the Dow sea water process, as operated at Freeport and Velasco in Texas, manifested itself during World War II.

This process has remained as the largest producer. The Texas operations take advantage of:

1. The economy of integrated plant operation where other products are taken from the water and where it may be used several times for cooling before the magnesium is removed from it.

2. The natural features of the terrain and local currents which allow discharge of the water at a nearby point where no dilution of the intake water results.

3. The low cost of electric power generated by the burning of local natural gas.

4. The ready availability of a basic precipitating agent in the form of oyster shells.[6-8]

A very economical sea water operation is also being carried out on Oslo Fiord in Norway, where hydroelectric power is economically available. This installation uses a modification of the I.G. process which was introduced by the Germans during their occupation of Norway.

The original Dow process was developed for the treatment of the very rich brines that are pumped from wells in the vicinity of the company's home plant in Midland, Michigan. The magnesium chloride was separated by fractional crystallization from the calcium and sodium salts which accompany it in these brines, and from then on the process was the same as from the evaporation step in Fig. 9.1a onward. This operation has been discontinued in favor of the Texas production.

The most basic difference between the Dow and the I.G. processes is the method of chlorination. The I.G. process, which was first developed to handle the mineral magnesite, creates dry MgO as the input to a chlorinator. The resulting product is anhydrous magnesium chloride, which the Germans realized would give them increased cell efficiency. The Dow process involves the neutralization of wet magnesium hydroxide filter cake to give a chloride from which water must be evaporated. The process stops short of complete dehydration because breakdown to the oxychloride and the oxide results at the limit.

The I.G.-M.E.L. process is nicely adaptable to the use of magnesite or brucite because it requires the production of MgO before chlorination. Such an adaptation was the basis of the Henderson, Nevada, operation of Basic Magnesium, Inc., during World War II.[9] Low-grade magnesite from Gabbs, Nevada, was concentrated by flotation to the purity suitable for the process. The oxide was then produced in kilns before briquetting and chlorination. The Basic Magnesium, Inc., plant had the largest rated annual capacity of any single plant yet built—50,000 tons. It was closed down at the end of the war.

The Dow process was adapted during World War II to use dolomite reserves in several plants in the United States. Diamond Alkali Co. integrated the dolomite treatment with other chemical processes in the Painesville, Ohio, plant. International Minerals and Chemical Corp. used dolomite, and other magnesium minerals in a complicated multiproduct process in plants at Austin, Texas, and Carlsbad, New Mexico. Here again neutralization, evaporation, dehydration, and electrolysis in the Dow cell were used.

An electrolytic reduction process which is a variation of the I.G. process is operated in Quebec by the Aluminum Co. of Canada. Russia has become a major magnesium-producing country along with the United States, England, Norway and Canada. It is the opinion of Major Ball, who has published rather complete information of the present and past world production picture, that Russia's magnesium is probably produced by the I.G. electrolytic process.[4] It is thought that 50,000 tons were produced in Russia during 1955. On the other hand, the production by M.E.L. in England has been strongly curtailed by the great increase in cost of electric power in that country. Wartime periods brought subsidies which temporarily reactivated large-scale production.

The intimate contact of the metal with the molten chloride electrolyte may lead to some entrapment of the chloride in the product of the electrolytic processes. However, this is a point of little concern, because the ensuing remelting and alloying processes are usually conducted with magnesium chloride-containing fluxes under conditions where the magnesium can be freed of such inclusions.

## 9.3    The Direct Reduction Processes

Carbon, silicon in the form of ferrosilicon, calcium carbide, and sodium have all been used as reducing agents in the production of magnesium. Carbon and ferrosilicon are decidedly the most important in the present economy. Some early work by the I.G. group on silico-thermic processes has been described by Ball.[4] The Pidgeon and the Bagley silicothermic processes, which are contemporary in North America, both use dolomite and ferrosilicon as raw materials. The Pidgeon process [10,11] has been used continually at the Dominion Magnesium Ltd. plant in Haley, Ontario, Canada, since the building of the plant in 1942. Five plants in the United States used the Pidgeon process during World War II, and four were reactivated during the Korean War. The Bagley process was developed and operated during World War II at Spokane, Washington, by the Electrometallurgical Co. As Fig. 9.2 shows, the only difference between the two silicothermic processes is the nature of the vacuum-furnace reduction. Whereas the Bagley process utilizes a large chamber with a cooled wall, the simpler Pidgeon process uses relatively small Fe-Ni-Cr alloy retorts at about 1150°C with a temperature gradient to allow the condensation of the magnesium at the cooler parts after its reduction and evaporation at the hotter lower end. One advantage of the silicothermic processes is the less rigid requirement on the purity of the raw materials than in the case of the electrolytic processes. High costs of fuel for the furnaces, expensive retorts and maintenance, the expense of the high-grade ferrosilicon, and the cost of vacuum are disadvantages.

The Hansgirg carbothermic process, which was operated on a large scale during World War II at Permanente, California, employs a unique but rather hazardous series of steps.[12] The flow chart of this process is presented in Fig. 9.3. The briquettes of mixed magnesium oxide and carbon are reacted in an arc furnace at about 2000°C to produce a gas mixture of magnesium and carbon monoxide. This mixture is shock-cooled in natural gas to prevent reversal of the reaction. The final vacuum-distillation step is necessary to remove the organic material and otherwise purify the magnesium. The final product exhibits a purity comparable with silicothermic magnesium. However, an additional step is needed to obtain it, and the fire and explosion hazards are greater than in the Pidgeon process. The hazards result

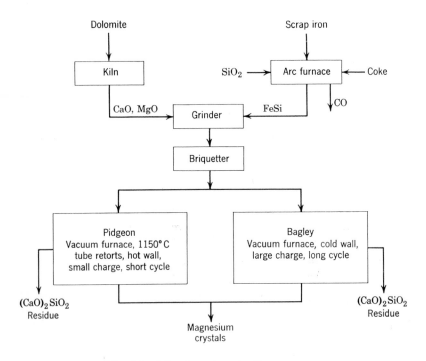

Fig. 9.2.   Silicothermic reduction processes.

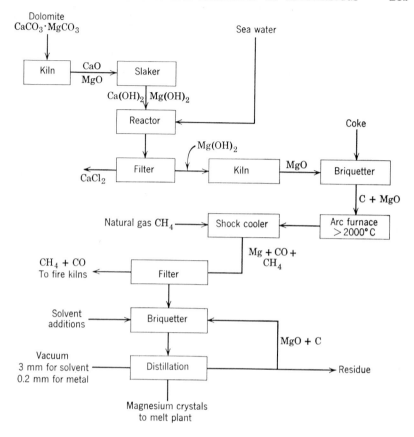

Fig. 9.3. Modified Hansgirg carbothermic reduction process as practiced at Permanente, California.

primarily from pyrophoric characteristics of the 0.1–0.6 $\mu$ particle-size magnesium powder after reduction.

## 9.4  Production

As has been pointed out by Ball,[4] the two lowest cost producers, The Dow Chemical Company in the United States and Norsk-Hydro of Norway, both use electrolytic processes under conditions of great natural advantage.  However, users of the direct reduction processes, in particular Dominion Magnesium Ltd. of Canada, are devoting much research effort to improve their natural production advantage.  It is

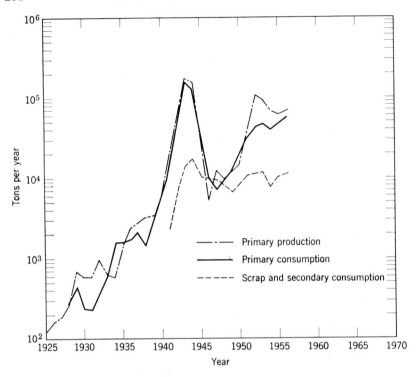

Fig. 9.4. Magnesium production and consumption in the United States.[13]

possible that one of the direct processes may eventually undercut the electrolytic process costs.

The great productive capacity of the world for magnesium was clearly demonstrated by the peak of output during 1943—225,000 tons. The growth of United States magnesium production from 1925 to the present, Fig. 9.4, represents the majority of the world volume.[13] The commercial markets which could consume the large production existing at the end of World War II had not been developed adequately at that time. Thus, except for government stockpiling of primary metal, which continued at large volume for a few years, the production figures dropped radically in the period 1944–1946. The development of large-volume nonmilitary markets in the United States since that time has caused a recovery of consumption. If one eliminates the wartime "peaks" and fits the "background" with a linear growth curve on the semilog plot, one might predict a production of over

1,000,000 tons in 1970.  Growth of primary consumption, as shown in Fig. 9.4, has been increasing at about the same rate and should about equal production at that time.  Secondary magnesium consumption appears to have leveled at about 10,000 tons per year.  Figures are not available for it before 1941.

The balance between the use of cast and wrought (mill) magnesium products in the United States over the period 1947–1956 is presented in Table 9.2.[14]  Although wrought-product use has increased greatly since 1947, it is still less than that for castings.

The end-use distribution data for magnesium products, as shown for 1956 in Table 9.3, reveal the balance of interest between structural and nonstructural application.[14]  Airborne structures were still the mainstay of structural magnesium in that year.  The cost savings from the use of magnesium in moving structures such as truck bodies, hand trucks, conveyors, luggage, jigs, and fixtures have caused the rise of tonnage in the other structural applications.  The trend of modern civilization toward more and faster motion away from the purely traditional association of strength and durability only with high-density materials has aided the commercial acceptance of magnesium.

Nonstructural uses outweighed structural uses by a factor of 2:1 in 1956.  The largest items are tied to the economy of the two other "newest" commercial metals—aluminum and titanium.  Each of these uses was significant when compared with the total structural uses.  Rapid future growth of structural uses depends mainly on the large-

#### Table 9.2.    National Magnesium Product Shipments, Tons

| Year | Total Cast | Total Mill Products |
|------|-----------|---------------------|
| 1956 | 18,084 | 12,690 |
| 1955 | 13,927 | 10,593 |
| 1954 | 12,889 | 6,872 |
| 1953 | 17,259 | 8,443 |
| 1952 | 17,429 | 9,125 |
| 1951 | 15,413 | 9,545 |
| 1950 | 7,612 | 6,405 |
| 1949 | 5,527 | 4,132 |
| 1948 | 4,680 | 2,933 |
| 1947 | 4,107 | 2,404 |

Table 9.3.    End-Use Distribution of National Magnesium
Shipments *

|  | Tons | Percent of Total |
|---|---|---|
|  | 1956 | 1956 |
| Structural Uses |  |  |
|   Aircraft and missiles | 11,300 | 16.3 |
|   Consumer products | 2,250 | 3.2 |
|   Electrical and electronic equipment | 950 | 1.4 |
|   Machinery and tools | 3,900 | 5.6 |
|   Materials handling equipment | 1,150 | 1.7 |
|   Surface vehicles | 1,050 | 1.5 |
|   Graphic arts | 500 | 0.7 |
|   Miscellaneous | 400 | 0.6 |
|     Total structural | 21,500 | 31.0 |
| Nonstructural Uses |  |  |
|   Electrochemical and chemical † | 7,300 | 10.5 |
|   Alloying other metals ‡ | 15,550 | 22.5 |
|   Metallurgical § | 20,100 | 29.0 |
|   Powder | 1,250 | 1.8 |
|   Miscellaneous | 50 | 0.1 |
|     Total nonstructural | 44,250 | 63.9 |
| Export (all forms) | 3,500 | 5.1 |
|     Grand total | 69,250 | 100.0 |

* Based upon interpretation of available data for all product forms in the form shipped to the indicated use. In some cases, metal apparently furnished for one end use may have been used partially otherwise, and this will not be reflected here. Shipments to the government stockpile are not included.

† Essentially cast and extruded anodes.

‡ Essentially for aluminum alloying.

§ Essentially for titanium production but including estimates for the production of other metals. In addition to metal purchased on the open market, the estimate includes that produced in a government-owned plant for the account of the government and that produced in "recycling" operations in titanium production, neither of which is included in official primary production reports.

volume low-cost production of wrought products, particularly sheet and extrusions.

## 9.5  Purity and Refining of Magnesium

A discussion of the purity of commercial metal should differentiate between *specification* and *typical or average analysis*. A specification is normally expressed as a group of maxima for certain elements which the manufacturer must not exceed. It may be set by the manufacturer and/or by an independent agency. A typical or average analysis, however, does not guarantee anything concerning the spread of purity of a product. It simply shows the routine purity, thus revealing the average production capability. Table 9.4 presents typical analyses, averaged over many samples, for electrolytic magnesium as produced without special precautions.[15]  The typical analysis of ferrosilicon produced magnesium also is shown in Table 9.4.[16]  The only present

Table 9.4.  Typical Analyses of Magnesium, %

|  | Electrolytic [15] | Silicothermic [16] | Sublimed [15] |
|---|---|---|---|
| Al | 0.005 | 0.007 | 0.0004 |
| Ca | 0.0014 | 0.004 | 0.001 |
| Cu | 0.0014 | <0.001 | 0.0002 |
| Fe | 0.029 | 0.001 | 0.0007 |
| Mn | 0.06 | 0.002 | <0.001 |
| Ni | <0.0005 | <0.0005 | <0.0005 |
| Pb | 0.0007 | 0.001 | <0.0005 |
| Si | 0.0015 | 0.006 | <0.001 |
| Zn | 0.003 | 0.01 | 0.005 |
| Other impurities | <0.03 * | <0.01 † | <0.01 † |
| Total impurities | <0.13 | <0.04 | <0.02 |

* B, C, Cl, K, Na, P, S, Sn—0.01 total; H—0.006; N—0.0025; O—0.0022; Ag, As, Ba, Be, Bi, Ce, Cd, Cs, Cr, Co, Hf, La, Li, Mo, Pb, Sr, Ti, W, Zr—<0.001 each.

† Ag, B, Be, Ce, Co, Cr, K, La, Na, Sn, Sr, Ti, Zr—<0.001 each; O, N, H not reported.

specification on this metal by Dominion Magnesium, Ltd., the leading producer of it, is the guarantee of a total iron, nickel, and copper content of not more than 0.005%.

Several purity levels are attainable in the production of magnesium by the electrolytic process. The five grades of purity in electrolytic metal offered by The Dow Chemical Company are presented in Table 9.5. The primary grade, with its maximum total impurity content of 0.2%, is adequate for normal structural applications of the metal. New markets for magnesium, particularly the chemical and metallurgical applications, such as reduction or alloying of other metals, have demanded higher purities. According to Krenzke et al.,[17] grades 2–5 are obtainable with the Dow electrolytic process by using singly or in combination the following methods:

1. Chemical treatment of molten metal.
2. Batch selection.
3. Chemical treatment of process liquors.
4. Changes in materials of process equipment construction.

The total metallic column has been inserted in Table 9.5 by the author. It is obtained by adding the "other metallic" total to the individual metallic maxima shown. It is implicit in the specification. Total *impurity* content is specified only for the 392–56 primary grade.

Electrolytic metal may be refined to a practical ultimate, typically 99.98%, by successive vacuum sublimations. This purity level is very difficult to exceed because of the limit of the zinc content which carries over so easily in the sublimation. It has been found that a third sublimation definitely improves on the second, but that no benefit results from any more work. Typical analyses of sublimed magnesium are presented in Table 9.4.[15]

Comparisons in Tables 9.4 and 9.5 indicate that metal of exceptional commercial purity can be obtained from either the electrolytic or the ferrosilicon reduction process. Values in Table 9.5 are specifications and those in Table 9.4 are typical analyses corresponding to which no complete and necessarily higher specifications have been set. Thus the purities of ferrosilicon magnesium and the purest grade electrolytic magnesium are comparable. The primary difference between them is the distribution of impurity levels. Aluminum, calcium, silicon, and zinc are appreciably lower in electrolytic than in ferrosilicon metal. On the other hand, the ferrosilicon metal has a slightly lower specified total level for iron, nickel, and copper (0.005%) than does the purest

Table 9.5.   Specifications for Primary and High-Purity Grades of Dow Electrolytic Magnesium, %

| Grade | Al | B | Ca | Cu | Fe | Mn | Ni | Pb | Si | Sn | Other Metallics | | Total Metallies | Total Impurities |
|---|---|---|---|---|---|---|---|---|---|---|---|---|---|---|
| | | | | | | | | | | | Each | Total | | |
| Primary * | | | | 0.02 | | 0.15 | 0.001 | 0.01 | | 0.01 | 0.05 | | | 0.2 |
| Mg2 | 0.004 | | | 0.02 | 0.05 | 0.01 | 0.001 | 0.01 | | 0.01 | 0.05 | 0.10 | 0.20 | |
| Mg3 | | | 0.003 | 0.005 | 0.03 | 0.01 | 0.001 | 0.01 | 0.005 | 0.005 | 0.01 | 0.08 | 0.16 | |
| Mg4 | 0.002 | 0.00007 | 0.003 | 0.004 | 0.03 | 0.004 | 0.001 | 0.005 | 0.005 | 0.005 | 0.01 | 0.07 | 0.13 | |
| Mg5 † | | ‡ | | 0.003 | 0.003 | 0.004 | 0.001 | 0.005 | 0.005 | 0.005 | 0.01 | 0.05 | 0.08 | |

* Total of all impurities 0.2% max; 99.8% Mg by difference.
† Tentative specification.
‡ Limited data on boron content indicate less than 0.00003%.

electrolytic metal (0.007%). However, these differences are minor in most applications.

A relation between manganese and iron in molten magnesium has been cited previously in this book. Specifically, it has been said that the higher the manganese content, the lower the iron content. This relationship holds only at manganese levels of several tenths to a few percent, however. Busk has cited a group of data which illustrate that below 0.1% Mn there is no unique relation between the two impurity levels.[18]

## References

1. J. L. Bray, *Non-Ferrous Production Metallurgy*, John Wiley & Sons, New York, 1947, p. 340.
2. C. R. Hayward, *An Outline of Metallurgical Practice*, D. Van Nostrand, Princeton, N. J., 1952, p. 403.
3. D. M. Liddell, *Handbook of Nonferrous Metallurgy*, Vol. II, McGraw-Hill Book Co., New York, 1945, p. 44.
4. C. J. P. Ball, "The History of Magnesium," *J. Inst. Metals*, **84**, 399 (1956).
5. A. L. Hock, "Magnesium Extraction from Fused Salts," *Magnesium Rev. and Abstr.*, **9**, 1 (1953).
6. R. M. Hunter, "The Electrochemistry of the Dow Magnesium Process," *Trans. Electrochem. Soc.*, **86**, 21 (1944).
7. C. M. Shigley, "The Plant of the Dow Magnesium Corporation at Velasco, Texas," *Metals Technol.*, **12** (April 1945).
8. W. P. Schambra, "The Dow Magnesium Process at Freeport, Texas," *Trans. Am. Inst. Chem. Eng.*, **41**, 35 (1945).
9. C. J. Ball, "The Basic Magnesium Enterprise," *Trans. AIME*, **159**, 285 (1944).
10. L. M. Pidgeon and W. A. Alexander, "Thermal Production of Magnesium-Pilot-Plant Studies on the Retort Ferrosilicon Process," *Trans. AIME*, **159**, 315 (1944).
11. A. Mayer, "Plant for Production of Magnesium by the Ferrosilicon Process," *Trans. AIME*, **159**, 363 (1944).
12. T. A. Dungan, "Production of Magnesium by the Carbothermic Process at Permanent," *Trans. AIME*, **159**, 308 (1944).
13. U. S. Bureau of Mines (published data).
14. "Selected Magnesium Statistics 1928–1956," *The Dow Chemical Company Bulletin No. 141–142*, Midland, Mich.
15. J. W. Fredrickson (private communication), The Dow Chemical Company, Midland, Mich.
16. Dominion Magnesium Limited, "High Purity Magnesium," *Bulletin No. T.I.B. 551*, Toronto, Canada.
17. F. J. Krenzke, J. W. Hayes, and D. L. Spell, "High Purity Magnesium," *J. Metals*, **10**, 28 (1958).
18. R. S. Busk (private communication), The Dow Chemical Company, Midland, Mich.

# Bibliography

J. Alico, *Introduction to Magnesium and Its Alloys*, Ziff-Davis, Chicago, 1945, 183 pp.

American Society for Metals, *Magnesium*, Cleveland, Ohio, 1946.

———, *Metals Handbook, 1948 Edition*, Cleveland, Ohio, pp. 967–1024. Supplement, 1954, pp. 73–79.

American Foundrymen's Association, *Magnesium Alloys Foundry Practice*, Chicago, Ill., 1941.

C. J. P. Ball, "The History of Magnesium," *J. Inst. Metals*, **84,** 399 (1955–1956).

———, "Magnesium Progress in Britian," *Light Metals*, **16,** 56 (1953).

———, "Magnesium in Britain—1954 and the Future," *Light Metals*, **17,** 42 (1954).

P. Bastien, *Le magnesium et les alliages ultra-légères*, Dunod, Paris, 1948.

A. Beck, *Magnesium und seine Legierungen*, Springer, Berlin, 1939. English translation *The Technology of Magnesium and Its Alloys*, F. A. Hughes and Co., Ltd., London, 1940, 512 pp.

A. W. Brace and F. A. Allen, *Magnesium Casting Technology*, Reinhold Publishing Corp., New York, 1957, 174 pp.

W. Bulian and E. Fahrenhorst, *Metallographie des Magnesiums*, Springer, Berlin, 1949, 134 pp.

W. H. Dow, "A Brief History of Magnesium in America," *Metal Progr.*, **55,** 675 (1949).

The Dow Chemical Company, Magnesium Department, Midland, Mich.:
*Machining Magnesium*, 1954, 63 pp.
*Magnesium Alloys and Products*, 1955, 86 pp.
*Magnesium Finishing*, 1955, 138 pp.
*Forming Magnesium*, 1956, 136 pp.
*Joining Magnesium*, 1956, 137 pp.
*Magnesium Design*, 1957, 235 pp.

F. A. Fox and G. Goddard, "Developments in the Production and Technology of Magnesium and Its Alloys," *Metallurgia*, **31,** 70 (1944).

## 224 MAGNESIUM AND ITS ALLOYS

*Gmelins Handbuch der anorganischen Chemie,* Verlag Chemie GMBH, Weinheim/ Bergstrasse, "Magnesium," A. 4.14, 1952.

W. H. Gross, *The Story of Magnesium,* American Society for Metals, Cleveland, Ohio, 1949.

S. I. Gubkin, L. N. Moguchii, and M. I. Zatulovskii, *Plastic Deformation of Magnesium Alloys,* Academy of Science of the U.S.S.R. Press, Moscow, 1955, 135 pp.

J. D. Hanawalt, "Industrial Significance of the Basic Characteristics of Magnesium," *Metal Progr.,* **49,** 548, 739 (1946).

J. L. Haughton and W. E. Prytherch, *Magnesium and Its Alloys,* Chemical Publishing Co., New York, 1938, 99 pp.

Magnesium Association, Summaries of papers at annual conventions, New York.

Magnesium Elektron Limited, *Magnesium Elektron Alloys—Design,* Manchester, England, 1958, 62 pp.

A. J. Murphy, *Non-Ferrous Foundry Metallurgy,* McGraw-Hill Book Company, New York, 1944, chapter on "Magnesium-Base Alloys," by F. A. Fox.

C. E. Nelson, "Neueste Entwicklungen auf dem Gebiet des Magnesiums," *Z. Metallk.,* **46,** 338 (1955).

Organization for European Economic Cooperation, *Magnesium Fabricating and Casting,* Paris, 1956, 83 pp.

E. V. Pannell, *Magnesium—Its Production and Use,* Pitman and Sons, London, 1944, 137 pp.

I. J. Polmear, "Developments in Light Alloy Theory and Practice," *J. Austr. Inst. Metals,* **2,** 167 (1957).

G. V. Raynor, *The Physical Metallurgy of Magnesium and its Alloys,* Pergamon Press, London, 1959, 531 pp.

U. S. Atomic Energy Commission ANL-5749, *Properties and Handling Practices for Magnesium: Literature Survey,* 1958, 132 pp.

# Index

Activation energy, of creep, 102
  of diffusion, 108, 102
  of precipitation, 122, 124
Age-hardening, 21, 117, 119, 120, 123, 127, 165, 173, 175
"Alligatoring," 172
Alloy composition, casting, 129
  wrought, 155
Alloy designations, ASTM, 127
Alloying to other metals, 204, 217, 218
Aluminum, alloying with, 19, 21, 28, 31, 44, 68, 71, 74, 116, 117, 119, 121, 122, 127, 128, 133, 137, 144, 159, 179, 180, 186, 189
  compatibility with magnesium, 201
Aluminum Co. of Canada, 213
AM100A casting alloy, 129, 134
Analysis, typical, 219
Anelasticity, grain boundary, 83, 95
Angles between crystal planes, 7, 8, 89
Anisotropy, elastic, 81, 95
  of diffusion, 109
  of electrical resistivity, 11
  of self-diffusion, 109
Anode efficiency, 199, 203
Anodes, protective, 199
Antimony, alloying with, 19, 61
Arsenic, alloying with, 30
ASTM alloy designations, 127
ASTM temper designations, 128

Atomic diameter, 18, 20
Atomic structure factor, 1, 3
Axial ratio, binary alloys, 26, 30, 32, 87
AZ31A wrought alloy, 203
AZ31B wrought alloy, 111, 155, 156, 157, 158, 159, 160, 163, 164, 165, 166, 167, 168, 171, 178, 180, 181, 189, 202
AZ31C wrought alloy, 155, 158, 159, 160, 180, 181
AZ61A wrought alloy, 155, 157, 161, 178, 180, 181, 198
AZ63A casting alloy, 120, 129, 130, 134, 139, 200
AZ80A wrought alloy, 115, 155, 157, 161, 166, 167, 178, 181
AZ81A casting alloy, 129, 130, 134
AZ91A casting alloy, 129, 130, 134, 151
AZ91B casting alloy, 129, 130, 134, 151
AZ91C casting alloy, 129, 130, 134, 151
AZ92A casting alloy, 120, 129, 130, 131, 132, 133, 134, 137, 139

Backfill, protective anode, 200
Bagley silicothermic process, 213
Banding, compression, 94, 111, 113, 172, 175
Barium, alloying with, 30, 36, 46
Basic Magnesium, Inc., 212
Bearing strength, 133
Bend plane, 90

Beryllium, alloying with, 144, 201
Bismuth, alloying with, 28, 47
Body-centered cubic solution, 33, 38
Boiling point, 11
Breakdown, ingot, 171
Brillouin zone, 14, 22
Brooks and Perkins, 154
Brucite, 208

Cadmium, alloying with, 28, 31, 37, 49
Calcium, alloying with, 36, 48, 68, 160, 173, 186
Canada, production in, 213
Carbon reduction process, 214
Carnallite, 208
Casting alloys, composition of, 129
mechanical properties of, 120, 130
Cathodic protection, 199
Cell formation, 88
Cellular precipitation, 117
Cerium, alloying with, 30, 35, 36, 50, 117, 118, 139, 186
Characteristic temperature, 11
Chlorination, alloy melt, 142, 148
Coherent precipitation, 117, 118
Coiling of rolled sheet, 171
Cold-chamber process, die casting, 150
Cold-extrusion, 177
Cold-rolling, 123
Cold-working, 111, 123
Columnar structure, 127, 135, 140
Compatibility, galvanic, 201
Compliances, elastic, 81
Composition, casting alloy, 129
wrought alloy, 155
Compounds, intermetallic, 20, 34, 37, 160
$CaF_2$ structure, 35, 53, 60, 62, 63
CsCl structure, 35, 38, 45, 51, 54, 56, 66
Laves phase, 36, 46, 48, 50, 51, 55, 60, 66, 123
Compressibility, 83
reciprocal, 82
Compressive deformation, 85, 94, 101, 113, 172, 181
Compressive yield strength, 133, 157, 179, 182
Conductivity, electrical, 13
thermal, 13, 127

Constants, elastic, 81
Continuous casting, 169
Continuous precipitation, 117, 119, 121
Copper, alloying with, 36, 51, 144, 195, 201
Core-making, magnesium foundry, 145
Coring, cast structure, 179
Corrosion, 195
galvanic, 201, 202
stress-, 198
Corrosion resistance, 133, 151, 198
Cracking, 102, 159, 173, 182
compression, 94
extrusion, 178
shear, 172
Creep-resistant alloys, 103, 118, 137, 140, 165, 168
Creep, tensile, 87, 101, 133
tertiary, 103, 105
Critical resolved shear stress, 95, 97
Crucible practice, melting, 142
Crystal structure, 4, 35, 37

Debye temperature, 11
Deformation, polycrystalline metal, 86, 90, 96
single crystal, 87, 89, 96
temperature dependence of, 83, 85, 90, 97, 98, 131, 163
Delay time, dry cell, 203
Density, 8, 127, 146, 149
change in freezing, 4
Density-of-states curve, 24
Diamagnetism, 14
Diamond Alkali Co., 212
Die casting, 127, 142, 149
characteristics of, 151
Diffusion coefficient, 108
"Directionality" of properties, 182
Direct-chill continuous casting, 169
Direct reduction processes, 213
Directions, crystal, 7
Discontinuous precipitation, 117, 119, 121, 137
Dislocation, partial, 84
Dispersion hardening, 117, 127
Divorcement of eutectic, 139
Dolomite, 208, 213

Dominion Magnesium, Ltd. (Domal), 154, 213, 220
Double texture, preferred orientation, 185, 188
Dow Chemical Company, The, 135, 140, 141, 154, 162, 168, 171, 173, 178, 201, 203, 204, 209, 220
Dow electrolytic process, 209, 211
Dry cell, 202
Ductility, 87, 95, 100, 102

Economy, foundry, 148
Efficiency, anode, 199, 203
EK30A casting alloy, 129, 139
EK41A casting alloy, 129, 139
Elastic constants, 81
Elastic modulus, 83
Electrical conductivity, 13
Electrical resistivity, 11, 12, 34
Electrochemical effect, solid solutions, 21
Electrolysis, 194, 209
Electrolytic metal, purity of, 219
reduction, 209
Electrometallurgical Co., 213
Electron concentration, 28
Electron states in atom, 2
Elongation, tensile, 133
Emission spectrum, soft x-ray, 25
End-use distribution, 217
England, production in, 213
Enthalpy, 9
Entropy, 9
Essex Aero, Ltd., 154
Eutectic divorcement, 139
Expansion, thermal, 11
Extrusion, conventional process and alloys, 161, 177, 178, 186
hollow, 179
powder, 116, 179
Extrusions, mechanical properties of, 157, 162
EZ33A casting alloy, 129, 131, 139

Fatigue resistance, 133
Fermi surface, 22, 24
Ferrosilicon reduction, 213
Films, corrosion, 194
Flux, compositions of, 141

Fluxes, melting, 141
Forging, process and alloys, 161, 181
Forgings, applications for, 182
mechanical properties of, 158
Foundry economy, 148
Fracture, 98, 100, 102, 174
Free-electron approximation, 14, 21

Gallium, alloying with, 28, 52
Galvanic corrosion, 201, 202
Gating, 127, 146, 148
Germanium, alloying with, 35, 53
Germination, 111
Gold, alloying with, 30, 35, 45
Grain boundary, anelasticity, 83, 95
cracking, 103
deformation, 95, 102, 139, 163
precipitation, 117, 118, 122, 139
Grain growth, 110, 116, 163
Grain refinement, 116, 127, 135, 140, 144, 159
mechanism of, 136, 144
Grain size, 111, 115, 149, 158, 172, 179
Grignard reagents, 205

Hall coefficient, 12, 34
Hansgirg carbothermic process, 214
Hardening, age-, 21, 117, 119, 120, 123, 127, 165, 173, 175
Hardening, interference-, 180
Hardness, 120, 133
Heat capacity, 9
Heat of vaporization, 11
HK31A casting alloy, 123, 129, 131, 140
HK31A wrought alloy, 156, 163, 164, 165, 166, 198, 202
HM21A wrought alloy, 123, 155, 156, 163, 164, 165, 166
HM31A wrought alloy, 155, 157, 165, 166, 167, 168, 178
Homogeneity, 116
Hot-chamber process, die casting, 150
Hot-cracking, 126, 137, 139, 148, 151
Hot-extrusion, 177
Hot-rolling, 171
Hot-working, 110, 159
Hume-Rothery rule, 17
Hydrogen, 123, 142
HZ32A casting alloy, 129, 131, 140

"Ideal" texture, sheet or wire, 183
I.G. Farbenindustrie, 135, 139
I.G.-M.E.L. electrolytic process, 209, 211
Impurities, principal, 195, 200, 219, 220
 tolerance limits for, 196, 200
Indium, alloying with, 28, 37
Ingot, 169
Inspection, casting, 148
Intermetallic compounds, stability of, 21
Intermetallic phases, cast ingot, 160
International Minerals and Chemical Corp., 212
Interplanar distances, crystal, 6
Ionic radii, 7, 29
Ionization of solutes, 30, 31
Iridium, alloying with, 30
Iron, alloying with, 52, 141, 195, 201, 222
Isotopes, 1
 radioactive, 108

Kinetics, reaction, 37, 122, 124, 198
Kink plane, 90

Lanthanum, alloying with, 30, 35, 36, 55, 138
Lattice parameter, 5
 effect of solutes on, 26, 30, 33
Laves phase, 36, 46, 48, 50, 51, 55, 60, 66, 122
Lead, alloying with, 28, 35, 60, 117, 118, 201
Linde's rule, 34
Lithium, alloying with, 28, 38, 56, 74, 77, 87, 117, 122, 127, 186, 189
Lubrication, roll, 171, 172
Luders bands, 177

Magnesite, 208
Magnesium chloride, 142, 209, 212
Magnesium Elektron, Ltd., 135, 140, 154, 209
Magnesium hydroxide, 194, 197, 212
Magnesium oxide, 198, 212
Magnetic susceptibility, 14
Manganese, alloying with, 30, 57, 105, 111, 117, 119, 124, 127, 142, 144, 159, 180, 186, 196, 222

Matthiesen's rule, 34
Mechanical twins, 84, 88, 94, 103, 116
Melting, heating methods for, 143
 safety in, 143
Melting pots, 141
Mercury, alloying with, 28, 35, 54
M1A wrought alloy, 155, 157, 159, 162, 178, 180
Microporosity in castings, 126, 136, 137, 139, 142
Mischmetal, alloying with, 139
Modulus, elastic, 83
Mold design, 146
Multiplicity of crystal planes, 6

"Negative difference effect," 199
Neodymium, alloying with, 138
Neutron capture cross section, 4
Nickel, alloying with, 30, 36, 59, 60, 141, 195, 201
Norway, production in, 212

Open-pot practice, melting, 142
Ordering, solid solution, 37, 43, 49, 56, 118, 123
Organic compounds, 144, 205
Orientation sensitive etch, 94, 187
Overlap, Brillouin zone, 14, 24, 28, 34
Oxidation, 126, 142, 144, 148, 198
Oxidation tendency, 127, 135, 142, 147
Oxygen, 123

Palladium, alloying with, 30
Paramagnetism, 14
PE alloy, 160, 204
Permanent mold casting, 127, 142, 149
Permanente process, 214
Photoengraving sheet, 160, 204
Pidgeon silicothermic process, 213
Pits, sublimation, 9
Plane wave methods, 22
Planes of crystal, 5, 9
 angles between, 7, 8, 89
 interplanar spacing, 6
Plate, mechanical properties of, 156
Platinum, alloying with, 30
Poisson's ratio, 83
Polarized light method, 94, 187
Pole figure, 184

Polygonization, aging by, 175
Potassium, alloying with, 55
Potential, standard electrode, 194
Powder extrusion, 116, 179
Praseodymium, alloying with, 35, 138
Precipitation, coherent, 117, 118
  continuous, 117, 119, 121
  discontinuous, 117, 119, 121, 137
  grain boundary, 117, 118, 122, 139
Preferred orientation, 108, 158, 182, 191
  development of, 94, 114, 187
Pressure die casting, 149
Primary metal, 216
Prismatic slip, 87, 189
Production, world, 216
Pumping system, molten metal, 168
Purity, 116, 219
Pyramidal slip, 87
Pyrotechnics, 205

Radii, atomic, 18
  ionic, 7, 29
Radioactive isotopes, 1, 108
Rare earth metals, alloying with, 127, 128, 137, 142, 163, 173
Recovery, 99, 103
Recrystallization, 103, 105, 110, 112, 137, 159, 163, 182
Reducing agent, 204
Refining, 219
Reorientation of grains, 94, 114, 174
Reserve cell, 202
Rhodium, alloying with, 30
Risering, 127, 146, 148
Rollability, 173
Rolling, cold-, 173
  hot-, 171
  warm-, 172
Russia, production in, 213

Safe melting practice, 143
Sand casting, 142, 145
Scrap, 216
Sea water sources, 208, 211
Secondary metal, 217
Segregation, effect of, 158, 172, 179
Self-diffusivity, 108
Semiconducting compounds, 36
Shear, twinning, 90, 92

Sheet, mechanical properties of, 156
Short-range order, 38, 187
Silicon, alloying with, 35, 62
Silicothermic metal, purity of, 219
Silicothermic processes, 213
Silver, alloying with, 31, 35, 37, 43, 127
Single crystal deformation, 85, 87, 90, 95
Size-factor, in alloys, 19, 21
Slip, basal, 85, 97
  deformation, 84, 97
  direction, 84, 88
  nonbasal, 85, 97, 103
Sodium, alloying with, 58
Solid solubility, binary, 17
Solutes, slightly soluble, 30
Sources in nature, 208
Specific heat, 10, 127, 146, 149
Specification, alloy composition, 129, 155
  purity, 219, 221
Spot test, alloy identification, 149
Stacking-fault energy, 84
Standard electrode potential, 194
Stereographic projection, standard, 9
Strain-hardening, 87, 95, 98
Strain rate, 102
Stress-corrosion, 163
Stress-strain curves, 96, 176
Strontium, alloying with, 35, 36
Structure factor, atomic, 1, 3
  crystal, 6
Sublimed metal, purity of, 219
Sulfur dioxide gas, 142, 148
Surface tension, 8

Temper designations, ASTM, 128
Temperature coefficient of resistivity, 11
Temperature dependence, of elastic constants, 82
  of elastic moduli, 83
  of plastic deformation, 85, 90, 97, 98, 131, 163
Tensile deformation, 99, 101, 103
Tensile strength, 133
Tensile yield strength, 133
Ternary alloy systems, 37, 68, 117, 119, 122
Thallium, alloying with, 28, 35, 65

Thermal conductivity, 13, 127
Thermal expansion, 11
Thermoelectric power, 12, 34
Thorium, alloying with, 64, 79, 80, 94, 105, 123, 127, 128, 135, 139, 142, 163, 173, 183, 186
Tin, alloying with, 28, 31, 35, 63, 117, 118, 127, 181, 201
Titanium, alloying with, 30
Transition precipitate, 117, 122, 123
Transition temperature, 100
Twin "bands," 91
Twinning elements, 89, 92
Twins, mechanical, 84, 88, 94, 103, 116
Typical analysis, 219

Uses, 218

Vacancy, 109
Valence, effect, solid solutions, 19, 21
  solute, 19, 21, 29
Vapor pressure, 9, 10
Viscosity, 9, 36

Warm-rolling, 172
Warm-working, 111
Welding, compression, 94, 174
Widmanstatten pattern, 119, 122
Wiedemann-Franz Law, 13

Work-hardening, 159, 163
Wrought alloys, composition of, 111, 115, 155
  mechanical properties of, 156, 163

X-rays, absorption edge for, 2
  absorption of, 4
  emission lines, 2

Yield stress, 95
Young's modulus, 83

ZE10A wrought alloy, 155, 156, 162
ZE41A casting alloy, 129, 137
ZH62A casting alloy, 129, 131, 136
Zinc, alloying with, 28, 36, 66, 71, 77, 79, 116, 117, 122, 127, 128, 136, 159, 161, 179, 186, 196
Zirconium, alloying with, 30, 67, 80, 127, 135, 144, 162, 173, 180
  incompatibility with other alloy elements, 141, 162
Zirconium salts, 135
ZK11 wrought alloy, 155, 162
ZK31 wrought alloy, 155, 156, 162
ZK51A casting alloy, 129, 131, 136
ZK60A wrought alloy, 155, 157, 162, 166, 167, 168, 178, 181
Zone theory, Brillouin, 14, 22